HALFTONE

PHOTOGRAPHY

for Offset Lithography

by
Erwin Jaffe

GRAPHIC ARTS TECHNICAL FOUNDATION, INC.
4615 Forbes Avenue   Pittsburgh, Pa. 15213

508                                   $6.00

FOREWORD

HALFTONE PHOTOGRAPHY is the second of a group of three photolithographic skills. The line photographer develops the basic photographic skills and techniques. The halftone photographer, having mastered the basic skills of line photography, becomes increasingly interested in more extensive scientific and theoretical knowledge of the photographic process. The color photographer adds to these two areas by approaching his work from a more artistic viewpoint.

This book was written for the young halftone photographer who is developing his knowledge of the process and for the experienced journeyman who desires a reference manual. The book not only discusses the "whys" of the process, but also the "hows."

Contrary to the approach of many writers on this subject, special attention has been given to the theory or theories of making halftones. A sound knowledge of the theories of the halftone screen is essential to its effective use and is also essential to understand the advanced techniques used in color photography.

Another area of knowledge that is essential to a competent halftone photographer is concerned with the original copy from which halftones are made. Without an understanding of the way that different types of copy are made and the materials used in their creation, the halftone photographer can never become a skilled craftsman.

Many areas in this book are the result of conversations with friends and working with associates. These extend over such a period of time that it is impossible to list all those who contributed, in some measure, to this book. However, a

few people deserve special mention for they did more than their share toward making this book a reality. They are:
  Jean Bourges, Bourges, Inc.
  Edward Brody, American Greeting Card Co.
  Herbert Paschel, Lithographic Consultant, New York
and last, but not least
  Rickie and Julius Jaffe
  Without the help, both technically and editorially, of the Lithographic Technical Foundation's Research and Educational staffs this book would not have been possible. But, within the Foundation, special thanks are due to Frank M. Preucil, Supervisor, Photographic Division; Jack W. White, Assistant to the Research Director; and Charles Shapiro, Education Director.
  The revisions in the third printing which includes new information on equipment and facilities as well as current instructions for making halftones with contact screens were made by Zenon Elyjiw and Jack W. White both of the Foundation's Research Department staff.

                                        Erwin Jaffe

December 1964

ACKNOWLEDGMENTS

The author, in his Foreword, has acknowledged the tremendous assistance we received in preparing the manuscript for this Skilled Craft Text. While most of the illustrative materials, tables, etc., are from the Foundation's Education and Research Department resources, it is our desire to give recognition to the outside sources of some of the materials we used. The names and specific points of help follow:

Army Map Service—Figures 59 through 63

L. P. Clerc, *Manual of Process Work*—Figures 27, 28, 65

Consolidated International Equipment and Supply Company—Figure 2

Douthitt Corporation—Appendix V

Eastman Kodak Company, *Darkroom Construction*—Figures 7, 43, 58

The Gevaert Corporation of America—Table VI

Henney and Dudley, *Handbook of Photography*—Figures 50, 53, 56, 57

Heubner Laboratories—Figure 64

C. B. Neblette, *Photography—Its Principles and Practice*—Figures 41, 42, 52

Herbert P. Paschel, *Modern Lithography*—Table III

Photovolt Corporation—Figure 44

Bruce E. Tory, *Photolithography*—Figures 24, 25, 31, 51

W. M. Welch Manufacturing Company—Figure 45

Natural Lighting Corporation — Figure 66

NuArc Company — Figure 67

Macbeth Arc Lamp Company — Figure 68

American Speedlight Corporation — Figure 69

TABLE OF CONTENTS

Foreword i

Acknowledgments iii

List of Illustrations xi

Chapter I Introduction 1

Section 1. Why a Halftone Screen is Necessary 1

Section 2. Types of Screens 2

Section 3. What the Halftone Screen Does 3

Section 4. The Glass Crossline Screen 4

Section 5. The Contact Screen 6

Chapter II Making a Halftone With a Glass Crossline Screen 8

Chapter III Making a Halftone With a Magenta Contact
Screen 13

Chapter IV The Camera Department—Its Equipment, Facilities and Tools 18

Section 6. The Lightroom 18

Section 7. The Darkroom 19

7A. Darkroom Entrances 20

7B. Darkroom Ventilation 21

7C. Darkroom Equipment 22

Section 8. The Arc Light 25

8A. Types of Arc Lamps 26

8B. Light from an Arc 27

8C. Types of Carbon Used 27

8D. Carbon Arc Characteristics 28

8E. Illumination Requirements of Arc Lamps 28

8F. Spectral Characteristics of Arc Light 28

8G. Hints on the Use of Arc Lamps 29

Section 9. Exposure Meters and Light Integrators 30

9A. The Exposure Meter 31

9B. The Light Integrator 33

Section 10.   The Photographer's Tools 36
Section 11.   Safety in the Camera Department 37

Chapter V   Description and Handling of Originals for Halftone
      Reproduction 39
Section 12.   Originals for Halftone Photography 39
Section 13.   Problems Associated With Various Kinds of
      Copy 40
      13A.   Pencil and Charcoal Drawings 40
      13B.   Ink Sketches 40
      13C.   Photographic Prints 41
      13D.   Watercolor Drawings 41
      13E.   Pastel Drawings, Crayon Drawings, and Oil
             Paintings 42
      13F.   Dye Transfer Prints 42
      13G.   Carbro Prints 42
Section 14.   Grouping of Originals 43
      14A.   Grouping of Originals by Size 43
      14B.   Grouping of Originals by Tonal Range 45

Chapter VI   Focusing the Camera 46
Section 15.   Ground Glass Focusing 46
Section 16.   Focusing with Calibrated Tapes 47
Section 17.   Focusing with Numerical Counters 50

Chapter VII   Viewing the Halftone Image 52
Section 18.   Dot Fringe 52
Section 19.   Evaluating the Halftone Negative 55
      19A.   The Highlight Area 55
      19B.   The Middletone Area 56
      19C.   The Shadow Area 57
Section 20.   Tonal Range on the Press 57

Chapter VIII   Principles of the Glass Halftone Screen 59
Section 21.   The Care of the Glass Halftone Screen 59
Section 22.   Ratio of Screen Ruling 60
Section 23.   Mounting Angle of Rectangular Screens 61
Section 24.   Screen Ruling and Tone Values 62
Section 25.   Focusing With a Screen in Position 63
Section 26.   Combination Line and Halftone Stops 65
Section 27.   The Theory of the Action of the Glass Halftone
      Screen 65

Section 28. Diffraction 67
  28A.   The Diffraction Theory 68
  28B.   Comments on the Diffraction Theory 71
  28C.   Conclusions on the Diffraction Theory 72
Section 29. The Penumbral Theory 72
  29A.   Glass Screen Operation as Explained by the
            Penumbral Theory 74
  29B.   Lens Aperture and Camera Extension Ratios by
            Penumbral Theory 75
  29C.   Lens Aperture and Dot Size by the Penumbral
            Theory 75
Section 30. Lens Stops 77
  30A.   The Iris Diaphragm 78
  30B.   The Waterhouse Stop 78
  30C.   The Square Stop 79
  30D.   The Dog-Eared Stop 79
  30E.   Special Stops and Stop Controls 82
Section 31. The Pinhole Theory 84
Section 32. Conclusions on Glass Halftone Screen Theory .. 84

Chapter IX   Shooting Halftones With the Glass Screen 86
  Section 33. Focusing the Screen 86
  Section 34. Screen Ruling and the Wavelength of Light 87
  Section 35. Screen Aperture to Screen Distance Ratios 88
  Section 36. Setting the Screen 89
    36A.   Setting the Screen With a Calibrated Wedge 89
    36B.   Screen Setting by Visual Focusing 91
    36C.   Screen Setting by Camera Test Exposure 93
  Section 37. Exposure 94
    37A.   Single- and Multiple-Stop-Exposure Systems 94
      37A-1.   Three-Stop Exposure Systems 95
      37A-2.   The Two-Stop System 97
      37A-3.   The Single-Stop System 98
  Section 38. Some Observations on Various Stop Systems ... 98
  Section 39. Miscellaneous Exposure Information 100
    39A.   Exposure Changes for Different Magnifications 100
    39B.   Angular Variation of Light Intensity 101
    39C.   The Use of the f64 Stop 103

Chapter X   Principles of the Contact Screen 106
  Section 40. Development of the Contact Screen 106

Section 41.   The Orange Contact Screen 108
Section 42.   The Magenta Contact Screen 108
Section 43.   The Gray (Neutral) Contact Screen 110

Chapter XI   Making Halftones With the Contact Screen 112
Section 44.   Contrast and Tone Range With the Magenta
            Screen 113
     44A.   The Controlled-Flash Method 113
     44B.   The Highlighting Method 117

Chapter XII   Densitometry and the Densitometer 120
Section 45.   Densitometric Terms and Definitions 120
Section 46.   The Relationship Between Density and Exposure 123
Section 47.   The Densitometer 128
     47A.   The Visual Densitometer 128
     47B.   The Photoelectric Densitometer 129
     47C.   Transmission, Reflection, and Combination
            Densitometers 129
Section 48.   The Practical Use of the Densitometer 130
     48A.   Calculating Evenness of Illumination 131
     48B.   Determining Filter Factors 136
     48C.   Exposure Calculation 138

Chapter XIII   Special Processing Procedures in Making
            Halftones 140
Section 49.   Etching and Chemical Reduction 140
     49A.   The Physical Action of Reduction 141
     49B.   Subtractive Reducers 142
     49C.   Proportional Reducers 145
     49D.   Intensification 146
     49E.   Special Hardener—For After-Treatment of Films and
            Plates 147

Chapter XIV   The Process Lens 148
Section 50.   The Nature of Light 148
Section 51.   Light Sources 149
Section 52.   Refraction 150
     52A.   The Law of Refraction 150
     52B.   The Index of Refraction 151
Section 53.   The Process Lens 151
Section 54.   Lens Aberrations 152

54A. Distortion 152
54B. Spherical Aberration 153
54C. Chromatic Aberration 153
54D. Coma 154
54E. Astigmatism 154
54F. Curvature of Field 154
54G. Aberrations and Lens Design 154
Section 55.   Image Distortions 155
Section 56.   Lens Resolution 155
Section 57.   Flare 156

Chapter XV   Filters 163
Section 58.   Filter Factors 165
Section 59.   Filters and Light 167

Chapter XVI   Special Halftone Camera Techniques 171
Section 60.   Screen Tints 171
60A. Light Sources for Tints 172
60B. Lens Flare and Screen Tints 173
60C. Vignetting 173
60D. Light Variation With Angular Distance 173
60E. Development Factors 174
60F. Suggestions for Better Screen Tints 175
Section 61.   Dropout Negatives (Highlight Negatives) 180
61A. Large Aperture Exposures 180
61B. Supplementary Line Exposure 180
61C. Sears Method 180
61D. Overlay Mask Method 181
61E. Other Methods 181
Section 62.   Re-Screening Halftones 182
Section 63.   Duotones 183
63A. Preparing the Copy for a Duotone 184
63B. Shooting the Primary Negative 184
63C. Shooting the Secondary Negative 184
63D. Variations on a Theme 185
Section 64.   Opaquing Masks 186
Section 65.   The Indirect Process of Making Halftone Images 187
65A. Procedure for Shooting the Continuous-Tone
        Negative 187
65B. Procedure for Shooting the Halftone Positive 189
65C. Hints for the Indirect Process 189

Section 66. Image Reversal _____190
Appendix I Density Table _____193
Appendix II Relative Exposure for Enlargement of
            Reduction _____196
Appendix III Fractions to Decimal Equivalents Table ____197
Appendix IV Metric-English Conversion Tables _____198
Appendix V Film Area Coverage of Circular Screens ____199
Appendix VI New Equipment Supplement, 1964 _____200
Index _____204

LIST OF ILLUSTRATIONS

			Page
Figure	1	Highly Magnified Section of a Halftoned Image	2
Figure	2	Production of Halftone Negative	3
Figure	3	A Glass Halftone Screen	4
Figure	4	A Circular Glass Halftone Screen	5
Figure	5	Magnified Section of a Contact Screen	6
Figure	6	A Typical Darkroom	20
Figure	7	Types of Darkroom Entrances	21
Table	I	Comparison of Darkroom Sinks	22
Figure	8	A Dot-Etching Table	23
Figure	9	A Simple Single-Arc Lamp	26
Figure	10	A Motor-Driven Arc	26
Table	II	Spectral Characteristics of Typical Arcs	29
Figure	11	A Typical Exposure Meter	31
Figure	12	A Typical Light Integrator	34
Figure	13	Proportional Circular Slide Rule	37
Table	III	Table of Approximate Lens Distances	49
Figure	14	Set-up for Bright-Field Illumination	53
Figure	15	Viewing Halftone Negatives	54
Figure	16	Set-up for Dark-Field Illumination	55
Figure	17	Diagram of Glass Screen Ruling	61
Figure	18	Moiré Patterns	62
Figure	19	Glass Screen Compensating Glass	64
Figure	20	Diffraction Theory of Dot Formation	67
Figure	21	Halftone Dots Exposed Through Screen	69
Figure	22	Umbra and Penumbra Areas	73
Figure	23	Halftone Dot Formation by the Penumbral Theory	73
Figure	24	Eclipse by Screen Ruling	74
Figure	25	Isolux Diagram Showing Dot Formation	74
Figure	26	Relationship of Lens Aperture and Dot Size	76
Figure	27	The Iris Diaphragm	78
Figure	28	Waterhouse Stops	78
Figure	29	The Dog-Eared Stop	80
Figure	30	Various Stops	82

Figure 31 Optics of the Crossline Screen   87
Table IV   Screen Distances for Various Screen Rulings   89
Figure 32 Aligning the Screen and Setting Screen Distance   90
Figure 33 The Finder Stop   92
Figure 34 Effect of Aperture on Tone Reproduction   94
Table V   Halftone Failures   103
Figure 35 Contrast Control with the Magenta Screen   109
Figure 36 Set-up of the Kodak Adjustable Safelight Lamp   114
Figure 37 The Kodak Graphic Arts Exposure Computer   115
Figure 38 The Du Pont Shadow Flash Computer   116
Figure 39 A Characteristic Curve   123
Figure 40 Areas of the Characteristic Curve   124
Figure 41 D logE Curve Variation Due to Development   126
Figure 42 The Time-Gamma Curve From Figure 41   127
Figure 43 Typical Visual Densitometer   128
Figure 44 Typical Photoelectric Densitometer   129
Figure 45 Combination Densitometer   130
Figure 46 Calculating Illumination on the Copyboard   132
Figure 47 Evenness of Illumination at Emulsion Plane   134
Figure 48 Action of the Reducer During Dot-Etching   142
Figure 49 Refraction of Light   150
Figure 50 Some Typical Lens Constructions   151
Figure 51 Pin-Cushion and Barrel Distortion of Square Copy   153
Figure 52 Spherical Aberration   153
Figure 53 The Field Curves of a Lens   154
Figure 54 Lens Flare Test   159
Figure 55 Calculating Percent Lens Flare   161
Table VI   The Properties of Light Waves   164
Figure 56 Wavelength Chart Comparing the Range of Sensitivity
           of the Eye and Film Emulsions   167
Figure 57 Filter Chart for Color Contrast Photography   168
Figure 58 Transmission Characteristic of a Filter   169
Figure 59 Fall-off of Light at Various Angles of Incidence   174
Figure 60 Relationship Between Stop Shape and Tint Design   175
Figure 61 Special Light Source for Production of Even Tints   176
Figure 62 Reflection Blinds Inside Camera Bellows   176
Figure 63 Size of Stop and Dot Size in Even Tints   177
Figure 64 Straight-Line Image Reverser   191
Figure 65 Action of the Prism Image Reverser   192

Chapter I

INTRODUCTION

The halftone screen is the basic tool of halftone photography. This piece of equipment and the techniques for using it open wide a new realm of photographic theory, imagination, and practices. With proper handling and understanding it will be a faithful servant towards helping the photographer have full command of his process.

1. WHY A HALFTONE SCREEN IS NECESSARY

In the operation of a printing press, an ink of a given color and density is transferred from the ink fountain to the inking rollers and then to the image areas of the plate. On an offset lithographic press, the ink on the image areas of the plate is then transferred to the offset blanket and from this to the paper. The ink that is printed is all of the same density or tone.

Now suppose, for example, we want to print a black-and-white photograph. The original is composed of a wide range of shades of gray, from near white to dense black. The various shades or tones are "continuous"; that is, they blend smoothly one to the other.

As we have seen, it is not possible for a printing press to apply different shades or tones of an ink to paper. Thus the visual effect of the continuous and varying tones in the original are achieved in another way.

The method by which continuous-tone copy is transformed into a printable image is by photographing the original continuous-tone picture through a halftone screen. The screen breaks up the continuous tones of the original into an almost countless number of tiny dots. These dots are equally spaced.

However, the size or diameter of the dots will vary according to the different amounts of light that were reflected from the different tones in the original.

When this halftone image is put on a press plate and printed, it prints tiny dots of ink. The ink printed by each dot, of course, has the same density. However, what we see is a combination of the inked dot and the white paper that surrounds it. Wherever the dots are small and the area of white paper is relatively great, the tone appears light. Wherever the dots are large and the areas of white paper around them are relatively small, the tone appears dark.

Figure 1   Highly Magnified Section of a Halftoned Image

2. TYPES OF SCREENS

There are two distinct types of screens used today for the production of halftone images. These are the *glass crossline screen* and the *contact screen*. Each of these screens has certain advantages and disadvantages, but the end result from either one is the same . . . the production of images made up of equally-spaced dots of varying size.

The glass screen is, as the name implies, a screen made of glass. In use, it must be kept at a definitely predetermined distance from the surface of the sensitive emulsion on which the halftone image is projected. The contact screen, however, is a screen made on a film support and is used in direct contact with the sensitive emulsion.

3. WHAT THE HALFTONE SCREEN DOES

On the process camera, light is either transmitted through a transparency or reflected from an opaque piece of copy. It then passes through the lens of the camera. It strikes the halftone screen before it falls on the light-sensitive emulsion that will become the halftone negative or positive image. When the light coming through the lens strikes the halftone screen, the light either passes through the clear portions of the screen, or is absorbed by the opaque portions. The glass halftone screen acts as a grating — allowing light to pass through the openings or blocking it in a previously determined pattern. The glass screen itself is a positive operating mechanism. It lets the light through, or it does not. There are no compromises. The contact screen, however, acts differently. It allows the light to pass through the different areas in varying amounts.

The various tones of the continuous-tone copy determine the amount of light that passes through the halftone screen.

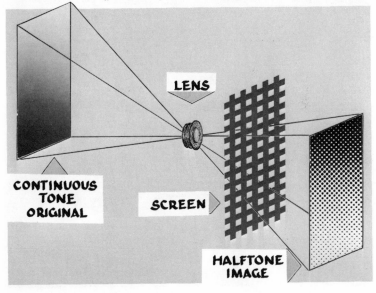

Figure 2   Schematic Showing Production of Halftone Negative

The smaller the amount of light that is reflected from or transmitted through a particular area of the copy, the smaller the amount of light that will pass through the halftone screen. These varying amounts of light are the main factor that determines the sizes of the dots that are formed on the film.

4. THE GLASS CROSSLINE SCREEN

The glass halftone screen (also called a "crossline" screen) is made up of two flat pieces of glass. Each piece has a series of black parallel lines on one surface ruled at an angle of 45° to the edge. The two pieces are cemented together in such a way that the lines on them cross each other at an angle of 90°.

4A. The Manufacture of the Glass Halftone Screen. Two flat pieces of glass, as nearly flawless as possible, are coated with an acid-resistant varnish. Each piece of glass is placed on a precision-ruling machine and a series of parallel lines are accurately cut through the varnish with a diamond cutter. The glass is then removed from the ruling machine and treated

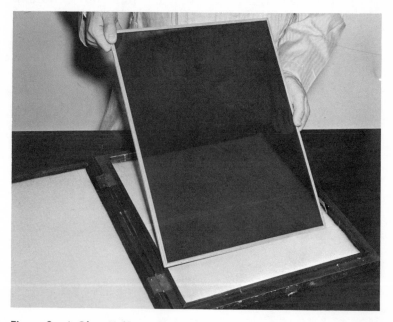

Figure 3   A Glass Halftone Screen

with an acid solution. This etches into the scribed lines to the desired depth. The glass now has a series of parallel grooves etched into one surface. These grooves are then filled with a black opaque material. Two such ruled glass plates are cemented together with their rulings on the inside and at right angles to each other. The cement most commonly used is called Canada balsam. An aluminum binding strip is placed around the edge to complete the unit.

The manufacture of a halftone screen is a precision job. The accuracy of the screen ruling is very critical. One manufacturer, for example, tries to keep the ruled lines within a tolerance of one one-hundred-thousandth of an inch (1/100,000). The need for this high degree of accuracy is caused by the ability of the human eye to detect even minor flaws in what should be an even tone. If one line is wider or narrower than another by even as much as one twenty-thousandth of an inch (1/20,000), the eye will be able to detect it in a flat tint.

Glass halftone screens are also manufactured in a circular form. The circular screen is set into a frame so that it can be

Figure 4   A Circular Glass Halftone Screen

rotated to change the screen angle. This is necessary in half-tone color-separation photography. The different halftone color-separation images making up a color picture must be produced with the screen at different angles for each of the colors to be printed on the press.

5. THE CONTACT SCREEN

Within the last few years the contact screen has become increasingly popular in the lithographic industry. In many plants it has completely replaced the glass crossline screen. Plants that cannot afford the high cost of a glass screen find that the less expensive contact screen adequately serves their needs for the majority of their black-and-white work, as well as some color work. The contact screen is not only less expensive in itself, but it also eliminates the need for screen bars and other devices that are necessary for using a glass crossline screen in the process camera. Contact screens cannot be used unless the camera has a vacuum back.

The contact screen is made on a film. It has a pattern of vignetted silver or dyed dots rather than the sharp lines of the glass screen. The idea of using a vignetted dot is not new.

Figure 5   Magnified Section of a Contact Screen

It has existed ever since the beginning of the halftone process. However, the proper films, developers, and technical know-how to produce a satisfactory contact screen were lacking until a comparatively few years ago.

Each vignetted dot in a contact screen represents an area that constantly varies in density from the middle of the dot to the middle of the clear area. When such a screen is placed in contact with a high-contrast emulsion and a continuous-tone image is exposed through it, the dots that are formed have the same varying size seen in the halftone negative or positive produced with the glass crossline screen. Contact screens can only be used in a camera which has a vacuum back. The vacuum is absolutely necessary to hold the screen in firm contact with the sensitive emulsion that is being exposed.

5A. Types of Contact Screens. There are two basic types of contact screens. One has dots of neutral gray dye and the other has dots of magenta dye. The magenta screens are most commonly used today. They are relatively inexpensive and durable with proper handling. Contact screens are made in sizes slightly larger than the standard film sizes that you use.

One type of magenta screen has a built-in highlight boost. It is used for black and white halftone negatives. Another type is used to make halftone positives from color separations. At one time, the Kodagraph Orange Contact Screen was available but it is no longer in general use.

Among the available gray screens, one produces elliptical or chain shaped middletone dots that blend smoother at the 50% area than the usual square dots. There are also a number of other types of gray screens for black and white work composed of wavy lines, concentric circles, etc., which are used for special effects.

Compared with the magenta screen, the gray screen has both advantages and disadvantages. It can be used with color originals since there is no color in the screen dots which can alter the colors in the original. However, the lack of color in the screen dots eliminate the ability to control contrast with filters which can be done with magenta screens. Other than this, gray screens are handled the same as magenta screens.

Chapter II

MAKING A HALFTONE WITH A GLASS CROSSLINE SCREEN

This chapter gives a step-by-step visual demonstration with parallel written instructions for shooting a halftone negative with the glass crossline screen. To the working craftsman, it may serve as a checklist. To the craftsman who is supervising on-the-job progress of a trainee in halftone photography, the chapter can serve as an outline. To the trainee this chapter serves to give a brief overall look at the job of shooting halftones.

As a suggested working procedure, the steps shown in this chapter can be used only as a guide. There is no insistence that the method shown, or the order of steps, will always produce perfect results. It is obvious that one typical, basic demonstration cannot cover all eventualities or guarantee that the method shown will be the best one for *all* people to use on *all* jobs. It is — to repeat — only a guide. However, it should be especially helpful to a photographer who is trying to learn, while on the job, with only limited help from a supervisor or supervising craftsman.

With this in mind, let us now follow this basic but useful method of making a halftone with a glass crossline screen. Full explanations of the "whys" and "wherefores," as well as the many variations and exceptions, will be found in later chapters of this text.

Let us assume that the copy is a black-and-white photograph. It is to be halftoned at same-size.

After cleaning the copyboard glass put the copy on the copyboard. Some photographers place it upside down on the copyboard so that it will appear right side up on the ground glass. If space permits always place a gray scale alongside the copy.

Pour developer into a tray and bring to the proper temperature (68°F) by use of a water bath.

Some cameras can be focused by means of calibrated tapes. This view shows the tapes being set at the indexing device located at the rear of the camera. Usually these scales are set for line copy. If a halftone shot is to be made, a revised reading must be used which allows for the change in the focal point caused by the glass screen being inserted into the optical path.

Set the screen into position and adjust it to the proper screen distance by using a calibrated wedge. Each corner of the screen should be the same distance away from the ground glass. For a 133-line screen, the distance from the screen ruling to the ground glass is approximately 15/64 of an inch.

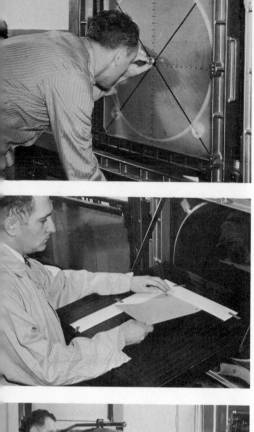

Center the image on the ground glass. Check the image to make sure it is sharp. A good 20-power magnifier is indispensable for checking focus. Readjust the arc lights for even illumination if necessary.

Turn off the white lights in the darkroom, leaving the safelights on. Remove one sheet of film from the box and place it in position on the vacuum back. Thin cardboard strips taped to the vacuum back assure film placement in the dark. Swing the vacuum back into position. You can now go out into the camera room through light-tight doors.

Adjust the lens diaphragm, and the integrating light meter to the estimated exposure time and make the exposure.

Now swing the flash lamp into position. Reset the diaphragm and make the flash exposure.

Enter the darkroom, open the vacuum back, remove the exposed film, and shut off the vacuum.

Check temperature of the developer. When it is correct, place the film in the developer solution in the following manner.

With your left hand, tilt the tray of developer forward.

Hold the film in the right hand and push it forward into the developer. At the same time, lower the left hand which is holding the tray. This creates a small wave of developer toward you. The film is actually pushed into the developer with the right hand by dipping the leading edge under the solution. The purpose of this procedure is to wet the entire film surface as quickly and evenly as possible.

Rock the tray front to back.

Then left to right. Finally, give the solution a gentle circulatory motion by alternately rocking the corners of the tray. Too much agitation will cause uneven development around the edges of the film.

After the designated development time has been reached, rinse the film in water and place it in the hypo solution. Let it remain here for a minimum of one minute before you turn on the lights.

NOTE: A rule of thumb for the time that the film should be in the hypo solution before lights are turned on is as follows: Note the time it takes for a test strip of the film to clear in the hypo. Developed film should be in the hypo solution for twice this amount of time before you turn on the lights.

Wash the film in water for 15 seconds and place it on a light table for inspection. Check the highlight and shadow dots as well as the entire tone scale. If the halftone is satisfactory, return it to the wash water for thorough washing before you hang it up to dry.

If your first results are unsatisfactory, place a new film on the camera vacuum back. Repeat the above steps with adjustments of exposure and development to produce the desired result.

Chapter III

MAKING A HALFTONE WITH A MAGENTA CONTACT SCREEN

The previous chapter presented a step-by-step procedure for producing a halftone with a glass crossline screen. This chapter will show the same operation but using a Magenta Contact Screen in place of the glass screen.

As before, this demonstration is not meant to be a single authoritative answer to handling contact screens. Rather it is presented as a guide to show a typical procedure using a different piece of equipment to produce a halftone.

Let us assume that the copy is a black-and-white photograph. It is to be photographed as a same-size halftone.

Clean the copyboard glass. Place the copy on the copyboard. Some photographers place the copy upside down on the copyboard so that it can be seen right side up on the ground glass. If room permits, always place a gray scale alongside the copy.

Pour the developer into a tray. Bring it to the proper temperature (68°F) with a water bath.

The camera can be focused visually. Check the sharpness of the image on the ground glass. With the contact screen there is no need to allow for the change in the optical path of the light through the screen, as it is negligible.

When the image is sharp, center it on the ground glass. If necessary, adjust your arc lights for even illumination.

Turn off the white lights in the darkroom, leaving the safelights on. Remove one sheet of film from the box and place it on the vacuum back. Hold it in position and turn the vacuum on.

Remove the contact screen from its box. Place it on the vacuum back over the piece of film that was previously placed there.

The screen should be placed with its sides parallel to the sides of the vacuum back. In this position the screen pattern that results will be at a 45-degree angle from the horizontal.

Smooth the entire surface of the contact screen into even contact with the flat of your hand.

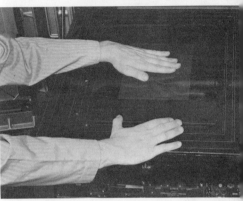

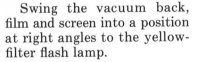

Swing the vacuum back, film and screen into a position at right angles to the yellow-filter flash lamp.

Now make the flash exposure. Notice that this is done before you make the image exposure through the lens.

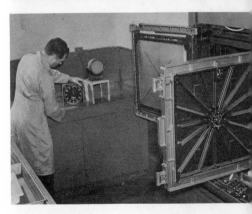

After the flash exposure, swing the vacuum back of the camera into the closed position to receive the image exposure through the lens. Don't touch the flashed film and contact screen.

Leave the darkroom through the light-tight doors. Set the lens diaphragm to f22. Set the integrating light meter to the estimated image exposure time.

Make the exposure.

Re-enter the darkroom, and open the vacuum back. Carefully remove the contact screen and replace it in its box. Now remove the exposed film and shut off the vacuum.

Check the developer temperature. When it is correct, place the film into the developer solution in the following manner.

With the left hand, tilt the tray of developer forward.

Hold the film in the right hand and push it forward into the developer. At the same time lower the left hand which is holding the tray. This creates a small wave of developer toward you. The film is actually pushed into the developer with the right hand by dipping the leading edge under the wave of solution. The purpose of this procedure is to wet the entire film surface as quickly and evenly as possible.

Rock the tray front to back and then left to right. Finally, give the solution a gentle circulatory motion by alternately rocking the corners of the tray. Too much agitation will cause uneven development around the edges of the film.

After the designated development time has been reached, rinse the film in water and place it in the hypo solution. Let it remain here for a minimum of one minute before you turn on the lights. *NOTE:* A rule of thumb for the time that the film should be in the hypo solution before you turn on the lights is as follows:

Note the time it takes for the film to clear in the hypo. Let developed film remain in the hypo solution for twice this amount of time before you turn on the lights.

Wash the film in water for 15 seconds and place it on a light table for inspection. Check highlight and shadow dots as well as the entire tone scale. If the halftone is satisfactory, return it to the wash water for thorough washing before you hang it up to dry.

If your first results are unsatisfactory, place a new film on the camera vacuum back, repeat the above steps with adjustments of exposure and development to produce the desired result.

Chapter IV

THE CAMERA DEPARTMENT – ITS EQUIPMENT, FACILITIES, AND TOOLS

The camera department is the section in the plant where the photographic operations take place. There are two basic types of operations — *lightroom operations* and *darkroom operations*. As the names imply, lightroom operations take place in an illuminated room, and darkroom operations take place in a darkened room.

6. THE LIGHTROOM

The lightroom operations are those concerned with the handling of copy, positioning the lights, certain camera operations such as adjusting the lens aperture and setting the exposure timer, writing up job tickets, recording time and other data for future reference. Other functions such as storage, packing and unpacking, may also be done in the lightroom.

The lightroom should be painted black; to repeat, black — a dull-finish black. This serves the purpose of absorbing as much of the stray light from the arcs and any other light sources as is possible. If the walls can absorb the light, then there is less chance that it will be reflected back into the camera lens.

LIGHTROOM EQUIPMENT. Obviously the basic piece of lightroom equipment is the process camera. In addition, there are usually miscellaneous light tables, stools, desks, storage facilities, and filing cabinets. The modern process camera is so designed that it is used partially in the lightroom and partially in the darkroom. Even though this type of camera is generally referred to as a *darkroom camera,* it is considered as lightroom equipment. In the case of a *gallery camera,* the entire unit is in the lightroom.

Aside from the camera and those controls which are normally in the lightroom, other facilities should include tables on which to spread out jobs, and a light table. This is required to register masks or multiple images, as well as for the inspection of dry negatives and positives.

7. THE DARKROOM

Darkroom work can be divided into two operations — *wet* and *dry.* The wet operations are those concerned with processing and the general handling of wet materials. The dry operations consist of such things as operating the camera, loading film, focusing, placing the screen, and so forth.

Many darkrooms are divided into a camera room and a contact room. This is usually done for ease of operation and to allow the two different operations to go on simultaneously. Occasionally, contact rooms are found in other departments of the shop, not under the direct control of the camera department or the photographer. This is usually the case in shops that specialize in the production of labels, or where many contacts are constantly required. In such a situation, the contact man is usually under the direct supervision of the stripping department. However, in our discussions in this book, we will consider contact operations as being a part of normal cameraroom work.

The darkroom should be painted *white.* The darkroom's safelight is so designed that a reasonable exposure to its rays will not fog the film being used. Even if this light is reflected from the walls of the darkroom, it is *not* building up the light to an intensity that will affect the film. When reflected from the walls, light from the safelight adds to the general illumination of the room and makes it easier for the photographer to work. The safelight being used, however, must be of the proper type for the emulsion being used. The data sheet, which is packed with different films, usually specifies the proper filter and lamp wattage for safelight.

The size of the darkroom will, to some extent, depend upon the size of the camera installed in it. Since the camera back swings open or down or both ways, enough space must be provided so that it will clear other equipment that is in

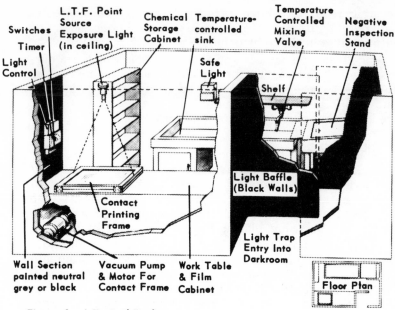

Figure 6   A Typical Darkroom

the room. For a camera up to and including 20" x 24", the minimum darkroom size should be about 9' x 9'.

This area is adequate for camera operation, but is not large enough for contact work also. For both camera and contact operations, the minimum room size should be about 9' x 15'. Naturally, a room larger than this would be preferable, but these minimum sizes will allow efficient operation.

7A. Darkroom Entrances. The entrances to the darkroom must be light-tight. In addition, you must be able to enter or leave the darkroom without permitting light to enter. Two such arrangements are the maze and the double-opening box, as illustrated in Figure 7. There are, however, a wide variety of other arrangements just as satisfactory. For example, the box-type entrance could have opaque curtains of velvet or rubberized cloth instead of doors. Various types of revolving doors will permit entrance and egress without difficulty. The two most common types of entrances are pictured.

It is often necessary to go in and out of the darkroom carrying wet pieces of film or plates or other items that are

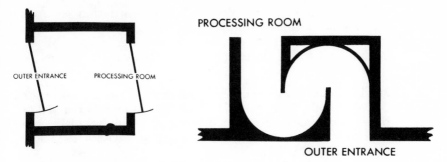

Figure 7   Types of Darkroom Entrances

clumsy to handle. For this reason the maze entrance offers the best solution. It allows you to pass through without touching anything, and with no need to relinquish your grip on whatever you are carrying in order to open a door.

The second best darkroom entrance is probably the double-opening box. This type offers a maximum space for carrying anything through the light trap. It is not always the total amount of available space that makes the passage through the light trap with a bulky item difficult or easy. This is governed by the wall arrangement within it. For this reason, the box-type of opening is sometimes preferred.

7B. Darkroom Ventilation. Basically, the darkroom is a closed-in room and it is necessary to provide proper ventilation. This is desirable for the comfort of the photographer, as well as his working efficiency. The primary requirement is that enough air changes be made within the darkroom. The general consensus is that the air in the room should be completely changed a minimum of six times per hour. If the room is arranged so that part of it is for dry operations and another part for wet operations, then the air intake to the room should be on the dry side and the exhaust should be on the wet side. This will keep changes in relative humidity down to a minimum.

The darkroom should be pressurized. In other words, fresh air should be pushed into the room so that the air pressure is slightly greater within the room than it is on the outside. The incoming air should be filtered. It can be allowed to flow out naturally through specially prepared vents, or it can be forced out. By forcing the air into the room through filters at a faster rate than it would ordinarily flow out, the dust problem is kept to a minimum. If the ventilation set-up is nothing more than a simple exhaust system, dust-laden air may seep into the darkroom through every crack in the floor, ceiling, and walls. Naturally, all ventilation ducts must be light-tight.

7C. Darkroom Equipment. The main piece of equipment in the conventional darkroom is the sink. It can be constructed of many materials such as wood, stone, or stainless steel. Each of these materials has its faults as well as advantages. These are listed in Table I.

Table 1
COMPARISON OF DARKROOM SINKS

	DISADVANTAGES	ADVANTAGES
WOOD -	Poor appearance. Inner surface accumulates slime	Inexpensive. Easily constructed.
STONE -	Very heavy. Susceptible to cracking.	Impervious to most photo solutions.
STAINLESS STEEL -	Expensive. Must be proper type of metal (type 316 or 317 of 18-8 s.s.)	Excellent appearance. Easily cleaned. Impervious to most photo solutions.

Although plans for the construction of darkroom sinks are available, most of them which are purchased are already made. In buying a sink, your best assurance of quality construction is a reputable dealer.

In addition to the sinks themselves, there are certain pieces of equipment worth mentioning that are used in, near, and around the sinks. A water-temperature control is one such item. With the use of equipment of this type, the flow of water into the sink can be regulated for both quantity and temperature. As most of the developing solutions are used at 68° F, it is advisable — and a production time-saver — to have a temperature-control system installed at the sink.

A regulated system for controlling the temperature of the water is sometimes incorporated into the sink itself. In such an arrangement, the water within the sink is re-circulated through a controlled heating and cooling system. The temperature of the circulating water is automatically corrected to the setting on the temperature-control valve.

Another valuable piece of darkroom equipment is a dot-etching table. Basically, this is a light table that can be used to inspect negatives or positives during and after development. Such a dot-etching table is equipped with both safelights and regular white lights, as well as a water-wash system. This allows the photographer to wash down the negative or positive after it has been given a reduction treatment.

It is also essential that there be a place available to store trays. This can be under the sink or in a special rack built for the purpose. The rack should be in a handy location near the sink. The most common tray racks hold the trays in a vertical position. This allows them to drain when put away wet and, in addition, makes tray selection easy.

Developing trays should be kept in all the standard sizes that will be used. In general, it is best to have at least two

Figure 8   A Dot-Etching Table

trays of each size. These are in addition to the wash tray and the hypo tray that are necessary in every darkroom. Trays are made of many materials including stainless steel, enamel, hard rubber, plastic, and glass. Naturally, each photographer acquires a preference for a particular type. Although all of them will work, glass trays are fragile and so easily broken that they should never be used except in the smaller sizes. One particular advantage of a glass or clear plastic tray is that it can be set over a light table illuminated by a safelight. Halftone images can then be developed by inspection without taking the film or plate from the tray of developer. This is not recommended, but sometimes it is handy to be able to inspect films during development.

Here is a special note about safelights: In the safelight that is placed over the developing tray, use a bulb that is not frosted. Use a bulb in which the filament can be seen. When developing line shots, you can hold the film up for a few seconds and look through it at the filament of the bulb. As the developing progresses, the filament will become more and more difficult to see. At the moment that it can no longer be seen, the film is fully developed and can be removed from the developer. This system also works with halftone images. When you want to carry the highlight portion of the negative to the barest possible printing dot, look through the highlight area at the filament of the bulb in the safelight. When the filament just disappears, you will find you have the small dot that you desire. While it is useful, sometimes, to be able to develop by inspection, it is not a recommended technique. Real control is best attained by strict adherence to time and temperature specifications.

The storage of films and plates must also be carefully considered. A dry table is needed within the darkroom where the light-sensitive materials in actual use are handled. Probably the best method of storing boxes of films and plates is on a series of shallow shelves below the table top. These shelves must be shallow. If more than a few boxes of plates are stored one above the other, the weight of the pile becomes too great to easily remove a bottom box when this is necessary.

The halftone photographer is constantly using lith-type developer. Regardless of the manufacturer, this developer usually comes in two dry portions. These are made into two solutions that are mixed together just before use. The proper storage of these solutions for ease in use can become a problem. Many photographers mix five gallons of each solution at a time, and then pour the five gallons into smaller one-gallon brown jugs. They then pour, from the smaller jugs, the required amount of each solution into the tray. This is a clumsy and time-consuming procedure.

A much more desirable method is to store the stock solutions in tanks having built-in spigots. The stock solutions can be mixed in quantity in the tanks, and then tapped when needed. This method eliminates the waste of time in pouring from one bottle or jug to another. These large (five-gallon or larger) storage tanks or jugs are available from many manufacturers, and are made of various materials. Stainless steel and the new polyethylene jugs are both excellent because they are not affected by the chemical solutions used in the photographic department.

Miscellaneous darkroom items that are essential and useful are as follows:
1. Film drying cabinet
2. A timer with a large sweep second hand
3. Thermometers
4. A trimming board
5. Scissors
6. Scotch tape
7. Graduates (at least one with a handle)
8. Safelights
9. Plenty of polarized electrical outlets
10. Cotton
11. Squeegee
12. Cellulose sponge
13. Rags and paper towels
14. Stool

8. THE ARC LIGHT

The most common source of light for lithographic photography is the carbon arc. It is used mainly because of the brilliance of its illumination. A carbon arc gives a high light output of the spectrum to which normal blue-sensitive film responds. Basically, an arc lamp consists of two carbon rods in separate holders, connected in a series circuit with a resistance, and utilizing direct current. The carbons are brought together by a spring or balance arrangement. When the current is turned on, the carbons resist this current and pull apart. An arc is formed across the space between the ends of the carbons. As the current continues, the carbons become incandescent and produce a gaseous column that is also incandescent.

8A. Types of Arc Lamps. There are two types of arcs in general use today. One is the manually controlled arc and the second is the motor-driven arc. The manually controlled arc is being displaced today by the motor-driven arc. As the names of these two types of arcs indicate, the manual-control arc is one in which the carbons used in the arc light are adjusted manually to maintain the proper gap when in

Figure 9 A Simple Single-Arc Lamp

Figure 10   A Motor-Driven Arc Lamp

operation. The motor-driven arc is one in which the carbons are driven by a motor to maintain the proper gap.

8B. Light From an Arc. Two types of light are generated by a carbon arc. The first is light from the carbon itself, and the second is from the arc. This is similar to the light generated by a match or a candle where the wick or matchstick generates light of one color, and is surrounded, or topped by, a light of another color. The arc light, which is the light generated in the arc space between the two carbons, is rich in the blue violet and ultraviolet light to which lithographic films are most sensitive. However, the light from the carbons themselves is basically yellow in color and the illumination is radiated in a very irregular pattern. The bluish light generated in the arc space radiates almost equally in all directions. As the voltage increases the carbons are forced still further apart. The arcing space with its bluish arc becomes longer and produces a correspondingly greater radiation of effective illumination. Thus, it is the arc itself that is the main factor in generating the light that exposes the photographic emulsion.

As the light continues to operate, the carbons burn away. It is necessary, therefore, to have a means — either manual or automatic — for keeping the separation between the tips of the carbon rods fairly constant. In the simple arc lamp, springs or a balance device does this. During operation, a crater is formed in the tips of the carbons. The majority of the light comes from this crater. The color temperature of this light depends on the material used in the core of the carbon. A white-flame arc is approximately 5500° K at a brightness of about 13,000 candles per square centimeter. A hard core carbon will produce a light whose color temperature is about 9000° K.

8C. Types of Carbon Used. Plain carbon rods are seldom used in modern arc lamps. Instead, special carbons are utilized. These have a hole drilled through the length of the carbon and this core is filled with metallic salts. In the case of the white-flame arc, the core is filled with fluorides of the rare earths. The use of such carbons allows for a wide variation in the color wavelengths that are emitted as well as for a considerable variation in the amount of the radiation emitted. This will permit an emulsion of almost any color sensitivity to be exposed.

8D. Carbon Arc Characteristics. The carbon arc and the common incandescent lamp differ widely in their characteristics. In a carbon arc installation, a ballast resistance, or some other type of current-limiting device, must be connected in series within the curcuit, for as the current increases the arc resistance decreases. Additional increased current in turn lowers the resistance still further.

A ballast resistor in the circuit limits the amount of current that can be passed. It thus stabilizes the circuit and keeps the current from building up too high. With an increase in current, the arc length will be increased. However, the increase will be greater with an increase in voltage. With a change in arc length there is a change in energy distribution at different wavelengths. The color of the light will be altered when this energy change is in the visible portion of the spectrum. The halftone photographer who is using filters will find that this causes a change in the filter factors which were originally determined with light of another color produced by a different arc length.

8E. Illumination Requirements of Arc Lamps. Hatch[1] suggests the following illumination requirements of arc lamps: " . . . . The spectral energy distribution of the light source must be in the same range as the sensitive material . . . All processes need an illumination of even intensity over the entire work area. The lamp for camera use, generally being angled in at the copyboard, needs to produce a different type of light pattern than the lamp for printing, so as to avoid a buildup of light at the sides of the work . . . The arc should come up to full intensity in as short a period of time as possible, particularly if the exposure period is short . . . the illumination from a carbon arc lamp should have both stability of intensity and spectral energy distribution."

8F. Spectral Characteristics of Arc Light. With regard to the wavelength sensitivity of the materials that are used for the production of negatives and positives, the limits of the average orthochromatic material is from 3500A to 5500A. This limit is extended to approximately 7000A for panchromatic material. How various arcs meet this need is shown in the following charts modified from Lozier and Dull[2].

---

(1) A. J. Hatch "A Motor Driven Carbon Arc for the Graphic Arts Industry," TALI, *1st Annual Proceedings,* 1949.
(2) W. W. Lozier and R. B. Dull, "Carbon Arcs for Graphic Arts," TAGA, *Proceedings 5th Annual Meeting,* 1953.

Table II
SPECIAL CHARACTERISTICS OF TYPICAL ARCS

	VERTICAL TRIM PHOTOGRAPHIC WHITE FLAME	HORIZONTAL TRIM HIGH INTENSITY PHOTO #118	ENCLOSED ARC
Carbon size	½" x 12"	11mm x 8"	½"
Spectral Intensity - Microwatts/cm^2 at 1 meter from arc axis			
3200-4000 Å	680	4140	1700
4000-4500 Å	720	3830	180
4500-7000 Å	2220	9960	440
Spectral Radiation - % of input power			
3200-4000 Å	3.6	8.2	7.7
4000-4500 Å	3.8	7.6	0.8
4500-7000 Å	11.7	19.6	2.0

This chart shows both the superiority of intensity within a given wavelength range, and the efficiency in terms of the percentage input power radiated within these ranges by the high intensity arc. Only in the 3200Å-4000Å range does the enclosed arc approach the efficiency of the high intensity arc.

8G. Hints on the Use of Arc Lamps. To the photographer who handles arc lamps as part of his normal routine, here are a few hints and tips concerning their use which may be helpful:

1. Do not try to trim carbons (adjust them to equal lengths) or replace them until they have cooled off.

2. If the circuit does not contain an automatic circuit breaker, pull the switch before trimming carbons.

3. Keep the reflector clean of the fine powdery ash that is formed by the burning arcs. If you don't, the efficiency of your lamps will be cut down considerably.

4. See that breezes and drafts are blocked off and prevented from striking the arcs; otherwise they may flicker.

5. Do not attempt to move arc lamps when they are lit.

6. Do not stare directly at the burning arc to determine whether it is properly lit. The amount of light in the room, or the shadows cast by the copyboard, can tell you just as easily if a lamp is lit correctly without running the risk of damage to your eyes.

9. EXPOSURE METERS AND LIGHT INTEGRATORS

The photographer must know a few important things about the light that he is using. The main factor is knowing how strong it is — its intensity, in other words. This is one of the most important factors in the determination of exposure. He must also know if it fluctuates during the exposure that he is making. These two points are basic in the correct use of an exposure meter or a light integrator. It is true that there are other factors concerning light that are important, such as the spectral quality of the light source, and the evenness of the light upon the copy. Some of these factors are discussed in Chapter 14, Sections 50, 51 and 52. However, the most important questions in actual everyday work are: "How much light have I got?"; "Is the amount of light consistent during the entire exposure period?"; "What is the total amount of light during my exposure?".

At this point it is important to see why the amount of light that is falling on the copy is a factor that must be determined. Let us suppose that in a given plant there is a camera that has the lamps rigidly attached to the camera. These lamps are set at an angle of 45° from the copyboard and at a distance of 48″. The photographer is familiar with this arrangement and has standardized his exposure time. Now, suppose an oil painting comes in as copy, and it is necessary that it be photographed in such a manner that the brush marks stand out. In addition, because of the large size of the original, the lamps must be moved back at least two feet in order to illuminate the copy evenly. When the photographer sets the lamps so that they skim the surface of the copy, they are at an angle of 15° rather than the original 45°. In addition, the new position has placed the lamps 72″ away from the copy rather than the usual 48″. Under this arrangement of copy illumination, how can the photographer calculate his new exposure and be reasonably certain that he is right? The usual answer to this problem is trial and error. The photographer makes a test exposure and, on the basis of the test, makes a new shot to get the correct time. This method is time-consuming and wastes material.

A second approach is to calculate the intensity of the light falling on the copyboard by the use of formulas or charts that consider the greater distance and the new angle. This again takes unnecessary time. The only problem that actually exists is to determine the amount of light falling on the copyboard under this — or any other — set of conditions. It is here that the exposure meter is of value. It enables the photographer to determine quickly the intensity of light falling on the copy as a numerical value. From this figure he can quickly and easily calculate the exposure. All this can be done in minimum time. Although the exposure meter is not as accurate or adaptable to graphic arts work as the densitometer, it is capable of giving reasonable approximations of light values that are of practical value and use.

9A. The Exposure Meter. Most exposure meters in use today are photoelectric. This type of meter converts the light falling on a photoelectric cell into electrical energy which in turn activates a pointer that moves a meter scale. The value read is applied to a chart built into the unit to determine the correct exposure value and lens aperture.

Figure 11   A Typical Exposure Meter

The device is usually built around a selenium cell. One side of this cell is covered with a material that is sensitive to light rays. The light falling upon this cell is converted into electrical energy and transmitted to the indicator unit. This unit consists of a powerful permanent magnet, usually of a horseshoe shape. In the center of this magnet is located a small movable coil. The current coming from the photoelectric cell passes through the coil, and in doing so creates a magnetic field about the coil. The entire coil then acts as a magnet, and tries to rotate within the magnetic field created by the permanent magnet. Its rotating motion is held within certain limits by small springs which oppose this rotation. The pointer is attached to the coil, so that as the coil moves the pointer also moves. This pointer is moving over a dial face which indicates the light value. In some meters the value is directly in foot-candles. When the light is cut off, the coil is no longer energized, and it comes back to rest. The value on the dial face indicated by the pointer is then set into a small built-in computational device. When the film speed is also set in, the values shown will give the correct exposure-aperture combinations for the particular film being used.

The exposure meter can be used to measure light in ways similar to the densitometer. However, it must be understood that the exposure meter cannot even approach the accuracy of a good densitometer. This is due to the design, construction, and peculiar sensitivity of exposure meters. The difference in cost between an exposure meter and a densitometer is a graphic demonstration of the point.

There are a number of ways to use the exposure meter. The most common, probably, is to place a piece of gray cardboard with a reflection factor of about 18 percent (such as the Kodak Neutral Test Card) in the copyboard, and read the value on the meter. When a change is made in either the intensity of the light or the angle of the lamps, the meter will show this change and the new exposure time which allows for it.

The meter can also be used as a brightness meter to determine the evenness of illumination on the copyboard. For this purpose, the copyboard is completely covered with a piece of white paper that has an even reflectance over its entire surface. The meter is held so as to read the light reflected from various areas of the copyboard; for example, the center of the board and each of the four corners. These readings will show whether or not an equal amount of light is being reflected from each of these areas. In the event that all the readings are not the same, the photographer should adjust his lights until the meter readings taken at all points are the same. When this is done, the photographer will know that his copyboard is *evenly* illuminated.

The exposure meter can also be used at the back of the camera by taking readings from the ground glass. In this way the correct exposure can be determined regardless of the amount of reduction or enlargement that has been made. The procedure is as follows:

Set the camera to same size, and the lens to its widest aperture. Cover the copyboard with white paper and turn on the lamps. Now take a reading with the meter placed flat against the center of the ground glass and pointing towards the lens. This reading is your reference point. When you have done this, set the camera to the new desired size, either enlargement or reduction, and take a new reading. This new value can be used in a simple formula to determine the new exposure:

$$\frac{\text{Old reading (ft.-candles)}}{\text{New reading (ft.-candles)}} = \frac{\text{New exposure (sec.)}}{\text{Old exposure (sec.)}}$$

If the meter is sensitive enough a different method can be used. With this method, the exposure time is kept the same and the lens aperture is changed to compensate for the new conditions. As before, take a reading on the ground glass, but this time with the lens stopped down to the aperture you ordinarily use. This will give you the correct aperture for your standard exposure which you have previously determined through trial and error. Then, focus the camera to the new size and adjust the lens aperture to give you the same reading on the exposure meter. When this is done, the exposure will be the same for the new magnification.

A sensitive meter can also be used to determine how nearly even is the illumination falling on the ground glass. This is done in the same manner as was done on the copyboard, except that the readings are taken at many points on the ground glass. When the readings are the same at all points, the ground glass is receiving even illumination over its entire surface. If the illumination falling on the copyboard is even, it cannot be exactly even on the ground glass. This is due to the fact that the photographic lens transmits more light through its center than through its edges. Thus an evenly lit copyboard will project an image on the ground glass that has less illumination at its edges than in its center area. To create an evenly illuminated ground glass, it is necessary to light the copyboard so that it receives more light at the edges than in the middle.

9B. The Light Integrator. We recognize the exposure meter as a device that allows us to measure the quantity of light falling on or reflected from an object at a given time. But in lithographic work, our exposures are not of short duration and we must know, or compensate for, the changing intensities of the light over a long period of time. This time factor causes difficulty for, over a long period of time, there is no reason to believe that the intensity of the light will remain constant. As a matter of fact, there is more reason to believe that the light intensity will vary. Every photographer has seen the fluctuation of his carbon arcs due to such things as variation in line voltage, or a draft running through the camera room.

Under varying light conditions we cannot accurately control our total exposure for it will not be consistent. We cannot measure the quantity of the light at one time and then assume that it will be the same during the entire length of the exposure. Yet, this is a prime consideration for accurate duplication of results. So, to accurately control our exposures, we must find some means to get a predetermined total amount of light through the lens and registered on the sensitive emulsion. This is accomplished with an integrating light

Figure 12   A Typical Light Integrator

meter. It is an accurate instrument for measuring predetermined amounts of light.

One common kind of light integrator works in the following manner: A photoelectric cell is placed where the light will fall on it. The cell is wired into an electronic circuit containing vacuum tubes. When light falls on the cell, an electrical current is generated. The closer or more powerful the light source, the greater the current generated by the photocell. The generated current is stored in a capacitor until the unit — not being able to contain more current — discharges and causes an electrical pulse. This electrical pulse goes through a vacuum tube circuit which amplifies it until it is of sufficient strength to operate a relay. When the relay is actuated, it operates a timing mechanism which registers one unit on a counter.

As the original pulse is proceeding through the circuit, the photocell is receiving additional radiation from the light source and creating enough current to recharge the capacitor. As before, the capacitor eventually discharges and a second pulse starts on its way. The timing mechanism is constantly registering while the light source is on. The speed at which pulses register on the counter depends entirely on the *quantity* of light striking the photocell and is not concerned with the time that is involved. When the number of units that the photographer has previously selected is reached, the timer automatically shuts off the lamps. The meter ceases to operate until it is once again set, and the lamps turned on.

To this basic unit, circuits can be added to operate an electrically controlled shutter, a flash lamp, or various other items.

The advantage of an integrating light meter is that the total amount of light that falls on the sensitive emulsion during the entire exposure time can be controlled. An integrator set for two units of light allows twice the total amount of light to fall upon the sensitive emulsion as would result when the integrator is set for one unit. In the same manner, when the integrator is set for four units, four times the total amount of light falls upon the emulsion.

When the arc lights fluctuate, for one reason or another, the integrator will either speed up or slow down, but it will not shut off until the required total quantity of light has been registered. Thus, an exposure of 100 units might mean that on one day your exposure would take 100 seconds, and on another day it might take 123 seconds. But, regardless of the "clock" time it took, the *total amount of light* falling on the copyboard would be the same and, if no other factors were changed, the negatives produced would be the same.

This instrument gives us an important item of control — consistent exposure. At the present time there are so many variables in the lithographic process that consistency in any phase must be regarded as a benefit and an important factor in achieving both quality and quantity of production.

10. THE PHOTOGRAPHER'S TOOLS

The photographic operations are complex, and the photographer is called upon to perform many of them in the course of his work. He must measure, compare, and mark, to name just a few of these operations. To help him in his work, he should acquire the necessary tools to help him perform, easily and accurately, the many tasks that occur in normal operation. Although not complete, the following list of tools is suggested:

Etching needle — Necessary for scratching information into the emulsion of negatives. A simple one can be made by forcing a phonograph needle into a short length of dowel stick.

Grease pencil — Good for writing on glass, films, bottles, and other slick surfaces.

Gray scales — Useful as guides for tone values when shooting halftones. They should be stocked in both film and paper types.

Magnifiers — Have at least two, one for wet use and the other for dry use. The wet magnifier should have a plastic frame and be of approximately 10 power. This magnifier is used to examine images during development. It should not be of too high a power. A high power glass has a limited field of view which makes it difficult to see a wide image area quickly. The dry magnifier should be of approximately 20 power. It is used to examine images on the ground glass as well as for the critical inspection of dry negatives and positives.

Miscellaneous — Pencils, paper, india ink, etc.

Pen holder and pen points — Necessary when writing miscellaneous information on film emulsions with india ink.

Proportion ruler — Necessary for scaling copy. A slide rule could also be used.

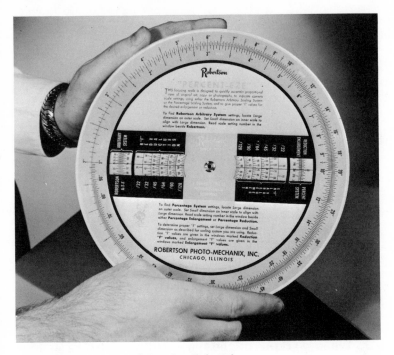

Figure 13   Proportional Circular Slide Rule

Protractor — Necessary for laying out angles on paper for certain jobs.

Push-pull ruler (At least six feet in length) — Choose the white face type of rule, as the markings can be seen more readily.

Screen separation wedges — A set of these wedges, covering a range from zero to one inch in 64ths of an inch, is an essential item.

Single-edged razor blades — Handy for many cutting jobs.

Straight ruler — This should be of stainless steel, at least 24 but not more than 36 inches long. The zero marking should not start at the edge of the rule, but should be inset a fraction of an inch. At least one inch of the rule should be divided into 64ths of an inch.

11. SAFETY IN THE CAMERA DEPARTMENT

There is always an opportunity for a careless man to become involved in an accident. The camera department offers as much chance as any place in the shop, so in general be careful!

There are so many things that could happen it is almost impossible to itemize them completely. Following are a number of suggestions that may save you from becoming involved in an accident:

1. Do not attempt to adjust arc lamps when they are lit.

2. Wait until arc carbons are cool before you start to trim them.

3. Don't touch electrical switches with wet hands. Dry your hands first.

4. Avoid splashing chemicals when mixing them.

5. Always wear rubber gloves and a protective apron when handling strong alkalies or acids.

6. Avoid inhaling dry chemicals.

7. Never add water to acids; always slowly add acids to water.

8. If you have sensitive skin, always wear gloves when processing film. This can prevent chapped hands or dermatitis.

9. Don't lean on glass-topped tables.

10. Carry and handle glass with both hands.

11. When working in the dark, put your hands out in front of you to prevent yourself from walking into walls or equipment.

12. Make certain that your hands are dry before grasping glass graduates. Otherwise they may slide through your fingers.

13. Always try to support a graduate with one or more fingers underneath the bottom when you are lifting it.

14. Don't carry too many bottles at one time.

15. Wipe up wet spots on the floor immediately to prevent slipping.

For additional information on equipment, see the New Equipment Supplement on page 200.

Chapter V

DESCRIPTION AND HANDLING OF ORIGINALS FOR HALFTONE REPRODUCTION

Copy comes to the halftone photographer in a wide variety of types. Among many other things it can be large or small, colored or black-and-white, or meant to be viewed by reflected light or by transmitted light. Regardless of the form of the copy, there are basic procedures which should be followed in handling it. But first let us see what are the most common types of originals.

12. ORIGINALS FOR HALFTONE PHOTOGRAPHY

PENCIL DRAWING — A drawing made with lead pencils.

INK SKETCH — An illustration usually made with india ink.

PHOTOGRAPHIC PRINT — An illustration in which the tones of the image are made up of black metallic silver held in suspension within a gelatin layer.

WATERCOLOR DRAWING — A drawing made with watercolors or inks. The watercolor itself consists of opaque pigment (tempera) or transparent dye carried in a water base. The color can be applied in the form of a wash on paper with a brush or an airbrush.

PASTEL DRAWING — A drawing made up with pastel crayons which consist of chalk and pigments ground into gum water and normally moulded into stick form.

CRAYON DRAWING — A drawing made with chalk, clay, charcoal, and/or colored pigments in a wax base.

OIL PAINTING — A painting made with opaque pigments ground into an oil vehicle.

DYE TRANSFER PRINT — A continuous-tone color print. The dyes used are in a water-soluble base.

CARBRO PRINT — A continuous-tone color print in which the colored pigments used are supported in a gelatin base.

COMBINATION DRAWING — A drawing in which the artist combines several art media and techniques such as india ink, opaque watercolor, and transparent watercolor in a single drawing.

SKETCH — Usually a quickly made preliminary rendition for any type of art. Sometimes it is used as original copy when the artist is trying for special, loose, casual effects.

WASH — This is one type of watercolor technique and may be used for the complete copy or applied over large areas such as a sky which is generally shown as an overall tone.

13. PROBLEMS ASSOCIATED WITH VARIOUS KINDS OF COPY

Having listed some of the types of copy that the halftone photographer must work with, let us go into a few of the details about some of them that make for easy or difficult reproduction.

13A. Pencil and Charcoal Drawings. Pencil and charcoal drawings are normally made on a roughened, textured paper. This paper has a tendency to further break up the granules of the lead or charcoal into smaller spots or specks. If these tonal areas are larger than the screen dots they cause no trouble, and the original effect is retained in the final print. However, when the dots are larger than these tonal areas, reproduction is poor, and the halftone loses the effect of the original drawing. For this reason, pencil and charcoal drawings should be shot at the same size or at only a slight reduction. When a great reduction is made, the results are poor and disappointing because the halftone dots are larger than the specks that produce the texture of the original. The drawing usually lacks contrast and a highlight dropout cannot be made without a highlight negative mask (see Chapter 16, Section 61).

13B. Ink Sketches. With most ink drawings there is little trouble, for the particles making up the ink are small enough to give the effect of a true continuous tone. The halftone screen does not break up this image to the point of resolving the individual colored particles, and therefore the picture can be well reproduced. One problem that does exist with ink drawings occurs when adjacent image tones are very close to each other in tone values. In this case there may be such a minor tone variation between these adjoining areas that the halftone screen cannot produce the necessary contrast to separate them from each other, and they will sometimes blend into a single tone area.

13C. Photographic Prints. Photographic prints are the most common types of copy supplied for halftone reproduction. In general, they reproduce well. When the photographic image is printed on rough-surfaced or textured papers, they do cause a problem because the texture breaks up the continuity of the tones. This is further exaggerated by the halftone screen and gives the appearance of a "jumpy" reproduction. This means that the tonal areas make too rapid a transition from one tone to another, and there is little or no smoothness. Sepia-tone prints are generally on textured or rough-surfaced paper and add to the problem because of their color. The best way to meet this particular problem is to have a print made on glossy rather than textured paper. In addition to a smooth glossy surface, a photographic print should have the full range of tones from bright white to a full-strength black for suitable reproduction. Soft, gray prints, as well as extremely contrasty ones, do not give good quality reproduction, although it is sometimes possible to improve the quality of the final result through intelligent use of various halftone techniques such as multiple-stop exposures or flashing.

13D. Watercolor Drawings. Watercolors follow pretty much the same pattern as ink drawings. It is often necessary to use filters to get the best relationship of tonal values.

A particular problem with watercolors arises when they include areas that are very pale, transparent, and almost the color of the paper. When the photographer tries to keep the white paper background and the pale tones separate, he cannot follow normal procedures. Additional contrast is needed in the highlight areas, and in most cases it is impossible to separate these tones with ordinary photographic techniques. To compensate for this, the halftone negative will have to be opened (reduced) in the shadow areas by the photographer or dot-etcher, or a combination shot may be required. In this case the photographer shoots to get the desired tone in the off-white colors, and makes an additional weak, underexposed, and underdeveloped negative to drop out the whites. The two are bound together in register. In some cases a combination line and halftone shot will do the job. (Check Chapter 16, Section 61 on special techniques for more details.)

13E. Pastel Drawings, Crayon Drawings, and Oil Paintings. Pastel drawings, crayon drawings, and oil paintings offer no special problem other than their color. First it is necessary to determine whether all colors are to be given equal tonal value or whether special colors in the original are to be emphasized. When the overall picture itself is desired, with no special emphasis on any particular color, the negative is usually made on a panchromatic emulsion. If reds are not important, then the copy can be shot on orthochromatic or blue-sensitive emulsions. The proper use of filters will enable the photographer to selectively drop out or emphasize particular colors (see Chapter 15). In addition, filters can be used with panchromatic emulsions in order to vary the color balance of the original.

Heavy brush strokes or strong canvas texture in oil paintings will sometimes create problems. These characteristics can be either emphasized or minimized by the use of proper lighting techniques. A minimum angle between the lights will minimize the boldness of the brush strokes or canvas texture, while a maximum angle between the lights (almost set to skim the surface of the painting) will emphasize them.

13F. Dye Transfer Prints. Dye transfer prints offer much the same problems as watercolor drawings, for the dye transfer print is basically a watercolor print. One particular problem develops with these prints when the retoucher works on the original with opaque rather than transparent colors. In such cases, the retouched areas on the negative will occasionally show up distinctly from the surrounding dye areas. This will happen even though the retouched areas are difficult to distinguish with the naked eye. When this happens, very little can be done other than extra handwork on the negative to bring the two areas to the same tonal balance.

13G. Carbro Prints. Carbro prints handle much the same as oil paintings. They offer no special difficulty and usually can be reproduced very well.

*   *   *

Occasionally the choice is offered to the photographer as to what type of color copy he would prefer. An advertising agency, for example, might have a dye transfer and a carbro print of the same subject and would like to know which one the photographer would prefer. If this is the case, it is usually better to request the carbro copy. When both the dye transfer and carbro prints are made by qualified personnel, prints will handle equally well. However, many of the dye transfer prints are made by semi-professionals or amateurs who are concerned only with producing a color image at a low cost. A number of these people turn out inferior work which may make the halftone photographer's job more difficult. Carbro prints, on the other hand, are made by a much smaller group of people. The majority of them are more highly skilled than the average dye transfer printer. So carbro prints are usually of better quality. In the event both types of prints are available for inspection, then the print which looks better will usually produce the better halftone negative.

14. GROUPING OF ORIGINALS

When a large number of originals are to be photographed at one time, the photographer will find it expedient to group as many of them as he can in order to save shooting time. In general, there are two methods of grouping, or ganging originals. The first is to group them together according to size, and the second according to type or tonal range.

14A. Grouping of Originals by Size. Of these two, the grouping by size method is of primary importance. There is no sense in making a shot unless it will fit layout. Therefore, the first step in shooting a large group of copies is to scale them to see by what size enlargement or reduction each piece is to be made. The original is measured, usually in the longest dimension, and the area into which it is to fit is also measured. By a simple mathematical formula, the percentage magnification is determined and marked on the copy. Notice that we have said the *percentage magnification* is determined rather than the magnification or reduction. This is done to simplify and express this size change with consistent meaning. For example, if the copy is to be reduced to half of its original size, then the photographer might mark "50%" on the original. However, when the time comes to shoot this copy there is the possibility that it might become confused with the group that is to be shot at one and one-half times its size. In a number of shops this size is designated as "1/2 up" and can, on occasion, be confused with the 50 percent reduction. To prevent this, a percentage magnification figure for all scaling of copy should be used.

Using a percentage magnification figure, all copy that is to be reduced will have a figure on it of less than 100 percent, while all copy that is to be enlarged will be greater than 100 percent. Same-size copy will be designated as 100 percent.

Determining Percentage Magnification. The percentage magnification is determined by substituting the proper values in the following formula:

$$\% \, M = \frac{\text{dimension of required negative}}{\text{dimension of original copy}} \times 100$$

Let us take an example. Suppose the picture area between two crop marks on the copy measure 9 1/2″. This is to be reduced to 4 1/2″ on the negative. Substituting in the formula gives

$$\% \, M = \frac{4.5}{9.5} \times 100$$
$$\% \, M = .4737 \times 100$$
$$\% \, M = 47.37$$

If the same 9 1/2″ length were to be enlarged to 12 1/4″, then the percentage magnification would be

$$\% \, M = \frac{12.25}{9.5} \times 100$$
$$\% \, M = 1.2895 \times 100$$
$$\% \, M = 128.95$$

In both of these calculations, the figures have been rounded off to the nearest 1/100 of one percent.

Notice that in working out these problems, the fractional parts of an inch were first converted into decimals. (A decimal equivalent chart is in Appendix 9.) In actual practice, a slide rule can be used to make these calculations, or a percentage rule can be substituted. The advantage of the percentage rule is that it allows you to set in the measurements as fractions rather than converting them into decimals. The end result, however, is the same. Percentage calculators are furnished with most cameras or can be purchased separately.

When scaling copy, the photographer should notice at the time he makes his measurements whether the final size must be exact, or whether there will be a little leeway. In the event he has a little leeway, he will find that he can group together copies that are within one-half of one percent of each other. For example, copies marked 58.39%, 58.89%, and 59.39% can be shot at the same time provided the camera is set at focus for 58.89%. Each of the other sizes are at the extreme limits of a change of 1/2 of 1% from this size. Naturally, this will vary in each shop dependent upon the tolerance that can be allowed. In some shops the photographer will be allowed a variation of only 2/10 of 1%. This means that, once the camera is focused to a given size, a copy that reads $\pm 0.2\%$ from this figure can be shot at the same time. When cropping, use the full width or height of the photograph, and favor making the size slightly larger to allow for masking by the stripper.

14B. Grouping of Originals by Tonal Range. The second method of ganging copy is according to type or tonal range. For example, suppose that you had two pieces of copy — one of them very flat, and the other slightly contrasty. To reproduce these reasonably well, you should shoot the negative for the contrasty copy a little on the flat side. In reducing the contrast, the end result will be more pleasing. With the flat copy, however, you will have to increase the contrast to get a negative suitable for reproduction. It becomes obvious, therefore, that if both copies were shot at the same time, you would have to sacrifice some of the quality in one or both of the negatives. For the best results, shoot negatives of such copy separately.

When grouping copies according to tonal range, therefore, it is convenient to use three broad categories: flat, normal, and contrasty. Assuming the size to be the same, you can place any shot in one of these categories, and with this arrangement rarely have to make more than three shots for a particular size group. It is advisable to use this method rather than try to shoot everything of one size in a single shot. When all types of tones of originals are grouped together and a single shot is made, quality suffers. Regardless of what else there is to say on the matter, the customer wants a good-looking job. Without a good negative to start the job, the press cannot turn out quality reproductions. If the job is based on group shooting, regardless of tonal range, then it is best to judge tonal range by mounting a gray scale with the copy and evaluating the negatives in terms of the gray scale image.

Chapter VI

FOCUSING THE CAMERA

After the copy is placed on the copyboard, the image is focused to the proper size and aligned in correct position to be exposed on the film or plate. The focusing operation is done in one of the three following ways:

1. Focusing on the ground glass.
2. Focusing by calibrated tapes.
3. Focusing by numerical counters.

15. GROUND GLASS FOCUSING

The oldest of the three methods of focusing the image is on the ground glass of the camera. This is done by alternately moving the lensboard and the copyboard, until the image is of approximately the proper size and is sharp when viewed through a magnifier on the ground glass. Once the image is sharp, the size is checked. If the size is wrong, the lensboard and copyboard are moved again to either reduce or enlarge the size of the image. When this new size of image is sharply focused on the ground glass, the size is again checked. This operation is repeated until the image is both sharply focused and of the proper size. Although these operations can be performed in a reasonably short time, it is not as rapid as either of the other two methods we will describe later.

There are certain precautions that must be taken with the ground glass method of focusing to insure that all the requirements are met. The first is concerned with the halftone screen. If a glass screen is used, its thickness must be compensated for in focusing. If a contact screen is used, this is not necessary. With the glass halftone screen, the image must be focused with a screen compensator in place. This is moved out of the optical path of the lens after the image has been sharply focused to the correct size, and the glass screen is then placed in position for the actual exposure.

Another point is the use of a magnifier to check the image. It must be focused to the underside of the ground glass. The simplest way to do this is to mark the innerside of the ground glass (the side nearest the lens) with a mark from a lead or a grease pencil. Then, with light passing through the lens for greater visibility, the magnifier is placed in position on the viewing side of the ground glass and is focused on the line that has been drawn. When this is done, the magnifier is locked. It is now correctly adjusted for focusing the image through the thickness of the ground glass. Now, when the image is projected onto the innerside of the ground glass and the magnifier is placed over a sharp detail of the image, the necessary camera movements can be made until the image is sharply defined in the magnifier with full assurance that the image will be in sharp focus at the emulsion plane.

The ground glass surface is a roughened one, and often makes a sharp line appear slightly fuzzy. For this reason, a center portion of the ground glass is often left clear. The focusing of the image for maximum sharpness is done through this clear glass area. In many shops an entirely clear glass plate is used to check for sharpness over a wide area.

A very efficient ground glass can be made from any photographic plate that has a "matte" surface. This surface, intended for pencil retouching, has a much finer grain than the commercial ground glass that is ordinarily available. To use such a photographic plate as a ground glass, first clear it in hypo solution. Then, with a razor blade, scrape a clear portion in the center of the glass approximately one-inch square. This glass is easily replaceable in the event of breakage. It makes an excellent viewing surface. The matte surface must be toward the lens in the same focal plane as the original ground glass.

16. FOCUSING WITH CALIBRATED TAPES

Most newer process cameras have some means of focusing the image by a mechanical method rather than by the more time-consuming ground glass focusing. One such method uses calibrated tapes. These tapes can be either rigid or flexible and are attached along the camera body. Indicators are mounted on the lensboard and copyboard above the tapes. If the indicators are attached to the lensboard and copyboard, they are so arranged that as these boards are moved, the indicators pass an indexing device usually located at the rear of the camera. Most of the newer cameras have the calibrations on the tapes so arranged that they can be read against an indicator located on the camera back and within the darkroom.

The construction of such a tape is not a hit or miss proposition. There are definite optical laws governing the distances from copy-to-lens-to-image-plane with the particular lens being used. When the focal length and other optical properties of a particular lens used in a specific camera are known, all the factors necessary for the construction of a tape are available. For various degrees of enlargement or reduction, the proper values are substituted in a formula such as the following which is used for single-element lenses:

$$\frac{1}{f} = \frac{1}{p} + \frac{1}{q}$$

where "f" represents the focal length of the lens,
"p" represents the distance from the copy to the lens,
"q" represents the distance from the image plane to the lens.

For magnification, the values are substituted in a formula such as the following:

$$M = \frac{q}{p}$$

where "M" represents the magnification.

These formulas are intended for simple lenses. When the more complex lenses that are used in process work are to be calibrated, additional information, such as the nodal points[1] of the lenses, is required. More complex formulas are used, and the calculation of the distance measurements to be placed upon the tapes takes a considerable amount of time and care to compute.

However, the fact is that these computations can be made, and the results engraved, etched, or written on a scale or

---

1 Nodal points — These are two points in a lens system located on the optical axis. They are so related that a light ray traveling in a given direction and entering one nodal point will exit from the other nodal point in a parallel direction.

Table III

TABLE OF APPROXIMATE DISTANCES (IN INCHES) BETWEEN LENS AND FILM "B", LENS AND COPY "A", AND THE TOTAL LENGTH BETWEEN COPY AND IMAGE "C".

SCALE OF FOCUS (Ratio of image to copy size)		FOCAL LENGTH OF LENS						
		10"	12"	18"	24"	30"	36"	48"
1-1 100%	b —	20	24	36	48	60	72	96
	a —	20	24	36	48	60	72	96
	c —	40	48	72	96	120	144	192
1-2E 200%	b —	15	18	27	36	45	54	72
	a —	30	36	54	72	90	108	144
	c —	45	54	81	108	135	162	216
2-1r 50%	b —	30	36	54	72	90	108	144
	a —	15	18	27	36	45	54	72
	c —	45	54	81	108	135	162	216
1-3E 300%	b —	13.3	16	24	32	40	48	64
	a —	40	48	72	96	120	144	192
	c —	53.3	64	96	128	160	192	256
3-1r 33%	b —	40	48	72	96	120	144	192
	a —	13.3	16	24	32	40	48	64
	c —	53.3	64	96	128	160	192	256
1-4E 400%	b —	12.5	15	22.5	30	37.5	45	60
	a —	50	60	90	120	150	180	240
	c —	62.5	75	112.5	150	187.5	225	300
4-1r 25%	b —	50	60	90	120	150	180	240
	a —	12.5	15	22.5	30	37.5	45	60
	c —	62.5	75	112.5	150	187.5	225	300
1-5E 500%	b —	12	14.4	21.6	28.8	36	42.2	57.6
	a —	60	72	108	144	180	216	288
	c —	72	86.4	129.6	172.8	216	258.2	345.6
5-1r 20%	b —	60	72	108	144	180	216	288
	a —	12	14.4	21.6	28.8	36	42.2	57.6
	c —	72	86.4	129.6	172.8	216	258.2	345.6
1-6E 600%	b —	11.6	14	21	28	35	42	56
	a —	70	84	126	168	210	252	336
	c —	81.6	98	147	196	245	294	392
6-1r 16%	b —	70	84	126	168	210	252	336
	a —	11.6	14	21	28	35	42	56
	c —	81.6	98	147	196	245	294	392
1-7E 700%	b —	11.5	13.7	20.6	27.4	34.3	41.2	54.9
	a —	80	96	144	192	240	288	384
	c —	91.5	109.7	164.6	219.4	274.3	329.2	438.9
7-1r 14%	b —	80	96	144	192	240	288	384
	a —	11.5	13.7	20.6	27.4	34.3	41.2	54.9
	c —	91.5	109.7	164.6	219.4	274.3	329.2	438.9

tape. These calibration marks are sometimes given in inches, or in percentage enlargement or reduction. At other times an arbitrary numbering system is used. Regardless of how they are made, they all express the same relationship of copy-to-lens-to-image-plane distances.

These tapes are used in the following manner:

The copy is first measured, and the desired percentage magnification is computed. This value is checked on a calibration chart and correct settings for the tapes are read from it. The photographer allows for the thickness of the glass screen if one is used. The copyboard and lensboard are then moved so that their indicators are set to the markings taken from the chart. Once in this position, the camera is accurately focused for the required percentage of magnification. If the tapes are calibrated in percentage magnification, this figure can be set directly onto the tapes without consulting a chart.

These calibrated tapes must be especially prepared for a specific lens, but once made and installed, they will save considerable time in focusing an image.

17. FOCUSING WITH NUMERICAL COUNTERS

Another mechanical system of focusing employs numerical counters similar to the counters found on a lithographic press. These are connected to the mechanism that moves the lensboard and copyboard. When these boards are moved, the counters rotate and register different numbers for different distances from a given point. The counters are calibrated in a linear dimension such as thousandths of an inch. Once the copy is scaled to determine the correct percentage magnification desired, this value is checked on a computed chart and the correct counter readings are found. The lensboard and copyboard are then moved until the counter readings are the same as those from the chart. At this point the camera is in focus and is at the proper size for the percentage magnification desired.

It must be remembered, however, that these calibrations are made for a specific lens. When another lens is used on the camera, another chart must be prepared to match the optical properties of the new lens.

*   *   *

There is no question that the use of a tape or a counter for mechanical focusing is essential when speed and many size changes are required. Although not a substitute for an accurately made tape or counter, homemade devices can be of advantage. Descriptions of methods of constructing simplified scaling systems are occasionally given in the trade literature[1]. The following brief description will give an indication of the reasoning and a method behind a simplified scaling system.

Although the photographer is called upon to produce negatives and positives over a wide range of enlargements and

(1) E. Jaffe, "Improve Your Offset Camera Procedures," *Inland Printer,* 135:3, page 52, June 1955.

reductions, he will, in most cases, find that certain sizes repeat themselves over and over again. Typical ones are same size as the copy, half the copy size, and twice the copy size. To eliminate the time consumed in trial-and-error focusing each time these sizes are called for, it becomes advantageous to paint or scratch reference marks on the camera rails so that these sizes are more quickly and easily located. This is an elementary scaling system.

Even though this operation takes time, it becomes a valuable timesaver when rush work is needed and several standard size changes are required. Naturally this system can create a multitude of reference points for many sizes, and it is a long and involved operation. However, it is a basic system that can be utilized if no tapes or counters are on the camera. With careful measurements of lensboard, copyboard, and ground glass to the scratched reference marks and the use of the formula previously discussed ($M = \frac{q}{p}$), a rough approximation of reference marks for other sizes can be made mathematically. However, the lack of knowledge of exact location of nodal points of the lens and other factors can only produce an approximation of an accurately calibrated commercial scale with this method.

Chapter VII

VIEWING THE HALFTONE IMAGE

The photographer may produce a halftone image and be amazed at the change that occurs in dot size when it is finally printed on the press. Often he will shrug it off with some remark about dot spread on a press due to printing pressures and pass the buck by saying that the pressmen should learn how to control their part of the process.

You've probably guessed that this was not written to pat the photographer on the back and sympathize with him about pressmen who ruin his beautiful dots. Rather, it is to point out another reason for dots getting larger in the shadow areas during their trip from the camera to the printed sheet. The reason is dot fringe.

18. DOT FRINGE

All halftone dots have a fringe area surrounding them. The width of this fringe will depend upon how the dot was made. When a halftone dot is made with a glass screen, the exposing light reflected from the copy goes through each aperture to create the core of the dot. However, the area around the central bright spot, that creates the dot core, is in partial shadow. This area receives only a portion of the light that creates the fully exposed dot core. It creates an area on the negative that does not contain as much metallic silver as the core. This is the fringe of the dot. Halftones shot in the camera directly will have the most fringe in the shadow areas on negatives and in the highlight areas on positives; contact dots will have the least; halftones that were dot-etched may have more or less fringe than a camera halftone dot depending upon the way that it was modified.

When a printing plate is made from a halftone with a wide fringe area, a minor change in exposure time can produce a considerable change in the dot size upon the plate. Here is the reason. When the plate is exposed, the fringe around the dot is also partially exposed, but may not be apparent on the developed plate. The dot may look to be of the correct size on the plate. However, when the plate is run on the press the fringe may eventually take ink which fills in the shadow detail.

Viewing Dot Fringe. To evaluate more accurately what the printing size of the dot might be, it is necessary that the photographer be able to see the fringe area around the dot. Even with a high-power microscope it can be difficult to see this fringe under ordinary illumination. However, if we change the angle of illumination, the fringe can be easily seen with a common 10-power magnifier.

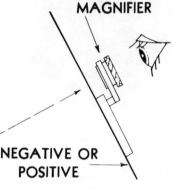

MAGNIFIER

NEGATIVE OR
POSITIVE

POSITION OF LIGHT
SOURCE FOR BRIGHT FIELD
ILLUMINATION

Figure 14   Diagram of Set-up
for Bright-Field Illumination

THE BRIGHT-FIELD ILLUMINATION TECHNIQUE. Bright-field illumination is the usual method of viewing an image of a negative or a positive under magnification. Figure 14 shows the relative positions of the light source, negative or positive being viewed, magnifier, and the eye.

Figure 15A shows a 50 times enlargement of a negative dot area that was developed in D-85 (a relatively soft developer), and viewed under the conditions of bright-field illumination. The fringe area is plainly noticeable.

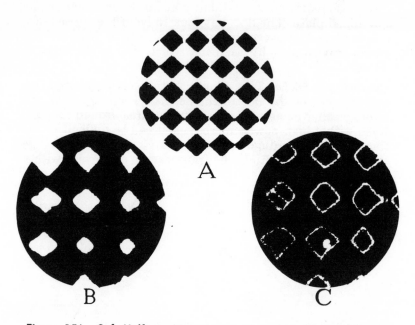

Figure 15A   Soft Halftone Negative as Viewed Under Magnification With Bright-Field Illumination Technique

Figure 15B   High Contrast Halftone Negative as Viewed Under Magnification With Bright-Field Illumination

Figure 15C   High-Contrast Halftone Negative as Viewed Under Magnification With Dark-Field Illumination

THE DARK-FIELD ILLUMINATION TECHNIQUE. When we use high-contrast materials developed in a high-contrast developer, we get a result such as the one shown in Figure 15B. Here the fringe is not noticeable, or only barely so. This would seem to show that we have a dot structure without a fringe. But when the angle of the illumination is changed, and the negative or positive is viewed against a dark field, as shown in Figure 16, we get a visual image that appears to be like that shown in Figure 15C. Here the halos about the dots are clearly noticeable, and could give us a closer indication of what might happen to dot size when the negative or positive goes into the plateroom to stand up under a powerful arc lamp. Because the image is viewed against a dark field this method is known as "dark-field illumination." Even though it is simple, it is an exceedingly good method for viewing the fringe area around the dots.

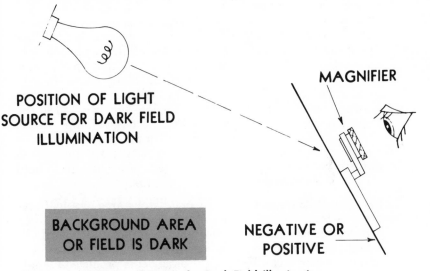

MAGNIFIER

POSITION OF LIGHT
SOURCE FOR DARK FIELD
ILLUMINATION

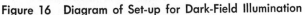

BACKGROUND AREA
OR FIELD IS DARK

NEGATIVE OR
POSITIVE

Figure 16   Diagram of Set-up for Dark-Field Illumination

19. EVALUATING THE HALFTONE NEGATIVE

In normal halftone work, the time of development for a particular emulsion and a given developer remains relatively constant. The dot size and the dot structure of the halftone image vary most with changes in exposure. In the case of the glass screen, dot size and structure vary most when screen distance is manipulated. However, regardless of the method used to produce the halftone image, once the negative has been processed it must be evaluated in order to assess its ability to produce the desired image on the printed page. In general, the photographer should evaluate the negative by assessing three areas — the highlight, middletone, and shadow areas.

19A. The Highlight Area. The highlight areas of the halftone negative are those that contain the darkest tones. The dark highlight area should be made up of tiny openings that will produce the desired highlight dot on the positive. The question that most often arises is "How small a dot should I try for?" The answer to this question varies depending upon many factors such as plate grain, cylinder pressure, paper surface, etc. However, in the vast majority of cases the highlight area of the negative should be capable of producing a positive dot of approximately 8-10%. Although the highlight area can be closed up tighter than this and produce a smaller dot, the resultant dot often has a poor structure and does not stand up well in platemaking. In addition, printed dots varying in size from the barest pinpoint to about a 5% value do not offer sufficient contrast with the blank paper stock to be of great value. This last statement, it must be realized, is a generalization. In specific prints where subtle detail in the highlight areas must be resolved for best visual appearance, this would not be a problem. So, although tiny dots can be produced in a highlight area, better results are more often obtained with a small dot whose size is large enough to hold up in the platemaking and press operations.

19B. The Middletone Area. The middletone area of a halftone negative is an extremely critical area because minor changes in exposure or development can create a considerable visual difference in the appearance of this area when reproduced. The middletone area can be thought of as being produced by dots that range from about 30%-70% in size. Too many photographers seem to worry only about the 50% dot without realizing that the middletone area covers a fairly wide tonal range.

The 50% dot marks the dividing line between connected and unconnected dots, and this distinction between connection or the lack of it is an important visual factor. In the highlight area a dot can vary a few percent in size and the difference can barely be noticed. But, where a few percent size change includes the range from an unconnected to a connected dot, the visual change is considerable. When you add to this the fact that the press operation will spread the size of the dot being printed, you get a further glimpse into the importance of this critical area.

The dots produced within this halftone range should cover all the tone values from 30%-70% with a smooth graduated change from one size to the next. The author has, as do other halftone photographers, certain preferences about handling the dot structure within this area. In my own case, the preference is for a halftone negative slightly *overexposed* in the middletone areas. This produces a positive having a slightly smaller dot size in the middletone area than is necessary. However, this takes into consideration the normal spread of the dot when being printed. Other photographers attempt to produce the exact dot size in their negatives and positives that they desire on the final print. They count on *perfect* plate and press reproduction. This is very rarely, if ever, really attained.

19C. The Shadow Area. The shadow area on the halftone negative should show a series of dots ranging from the barest pinpoint to approximately a 30% dot. These, when converted to the final positive image should reproduce a dot range from about 70% to almost 99%. Unfortunately, dot size on a negative or positive rarely reproduces as desired. Part of this problem we have mentioned earlier when we discussed dot spread by press cylinder pressures. Let us now add one additional factor, and then mention how dot size in the shadow area can be adjusted to control it.

The typical pressman is a conscientious craftsman who attempts to print on paper the image he has on his plate. Therefore, when he sees a small opening in the shadow area, he attempts to keep this open on the press. To do this, he is often compelled to change his ink-water balance or run his ink sparingly. The shadow area then carries an ink film that is too light and the end result is a tone far from black. The picture ends up reproducing too flat. All this because the photographer produced a good negative having a pinpoint opening in the shadow area of the final image.

The cameraman should anticipate this and produce a negative having about an 8%-10% dot in the dark shadow area. A dot smaller than this in the negative can create an unnecessary problem on the press. Then, for the darkest shadow areas, *no* dot should be produced. This arrangement gives the best contrast and visual appearance of the final product.

20. TONAL RANGE ON THE PRESS

From the previous paragraphs you should have noted the consideration given to the press and the pressman in discussing what would seem to be only a photographer's problem — the halftone negative! This point is of extreme importance in the evaluation of halftone negatives. The negative cannot be assessed purely from the standpoint of theory, but must rather be evaluated in the light of what happens to it in the course of printing the final image.

Evaluation of the negative must also consider analysis of the remaining steps in the process. The photographer must see press sheets and attempt to compare them with the negative or positive that produced the image. Only in this way can he develop judgment in creating the tone range and dot structure that will produce the desired press image.

Chapter VIII

PRINCIPLES OF THE GLASS
HALFTONE SCREEN

The halftone screen is the tool that converts the continuous tones and shades of an original copy into the halftone dots that can be printed and visually reproduce the original. The screen is a conversion instrument because it changes continuous tones to different values of halftone dots.

21. THE CARE OF THE GLASS HALFTONE SCREEN

The glass halftone screen is both a delicate and highly priced instrument. It should always be handled with care. When not in use, keep the screen in its padded case. If the case is kept in good condition, it will keep out dust and dirt. In addition, store the screen in a cool, dry place. Warm air will soften the Canada balsam used to cement the two halves of the screen together. When a shop has a number of screens, a convenient way to store them is to make a cabinet with a series of slotted, padded compartments into which the individual screens can be slid. When stored in this manner, the screens are usually removed from their original case. The compartmented cabinet should have a door that can be closed to keep out dust.

To get the best results from a glass screen, it is necessary that it be kept clean. Dust on the surface of the screen will lead to pinholes and blotchy areas in negatives. This can destroy the quality of otherwise evenly-tinted areas. Glass screens are made of soft glass. Just any haphazard method of wiping the screen may do more harm than good. Careless cleaning can scratch the glass surface and make the screen useless unless it is re-surfaced. This is both costly and time-consuming.

There are several ways to clean the glass surface properly. Here is one of the simplest. First brush the glass very lightly with a soft camel's hair brush to remove the loose surface dust. After this, dampen a wad of soft surgical cotton, a piece of lens tissue, or well-washed piece of soft linen with an Ivory soap and water solution. Wipe this dampened pad over the surface of the screen. Use a second dry pad to remove the moisture. Finally, you breathe on the surface of the glass to dampen it and then wipe it dry with a pad of any of the materials previously mentioned.

CAUTION: When cleaning a screen, the wet pads should do nothing more than barely *moisten* the surface of the glass. An excess of liquid can soak under the binding edge and in between the screen halves, causing them to separate. It is advisable, therefore, to wring out the pads before they are applied to the screen to eliminate any excess moisture.

Do not, under any circumstances, try to clean the screen with only a dry cloth or lens tissue. The dry pad rubbing against the dry glass surface of the screen creates friction and generates static electricity. With this condition, the surface of the screen acts as a magnet and draws the dust particles to it. More dust will cling to the surface than can be removed by the rubbing operation. And, as mentioned before, cleaning with a dry pad, no matter how soft, can cause scratches.

Occasionally, a screen may develop a crack due to accident or mishandling. If this occurs, the crack will creep and gradually increase in size as the screen is used. To stop this, the screen manufacturer, an optical laboratory, or a well-equipped optician can bore a tiny hole through the screen at the very end of the crack. This will stop the creeping. If the crack does not fall within the usable area, it will allow the continued use of an expensive piece of equipment that might otherwise become useless.

22. RATIO OF SCREEN RULING

When a halftone screen is ruled, the ratio of the width of the ruled line to the clear space can be varied. Although for special purposes the screen can be made with a black ruled line two or three times wider than the clear space. The most common ratio is 1:1. This means that the width of the opaque line is equal to the width of the clear transparent line. Thus,

$$A = B = C = D = E = F = G$$

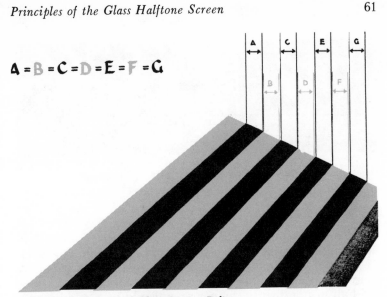

Figure 17   Diagram of Glass Screen Ruling

a screen having a 150-line ruling would have 150 opaque lines and 150 clear lines per inch. Each line — either opaque or clear — would then be 1/300 of an inch wide. It has been suggested that the common 1:1 ratio that is used in lithography is not the best for lithographic purposes and that it would be preferable to have the clear and opaque strips in the ratio of 8:5[1].

23. MOUNTING ANGLE OF RECTANGULAR SCREENS

Rectangular screens are mounted so that their lines run at an angle of 45° from the vertical. This is done because it is easier for the human eye to see patterns in groups of lines or dots that are horizontal or vertical than to see the same pattern when it is at an angle of 45°. In addition, our normal mode of construction produces lines that are vertical or horizontal (think of skyscrapers, window frames, and the framework of buildings, for example). If the screen were mounted with its line vertical or horizontal, it would be more apt to create a disturbing pattern (known as a moiré pattern) between the lines of the subject being reproduced and the pattern of the screen.

---

(1) V. G. W. Harrison, "The Theory of the Halftone Screen: A Study in Diffraction," *Photographic Journal,* 92B:74, 1952.

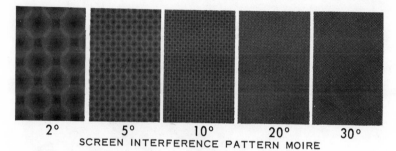

2°   5°   10°   20°   30°

SCREEN INTERFERENCE PATTERN MOIRE

Figure 18   Moiré Patterns

24. SCREEN RULING AND TONE VALUES

The highlight, middletone, and shadow areas of a halftone reproduction are determined by the size relationship between the printed dot and the non-printed area of the paper. A typical checkerboard pattern consisting half of printed dots and half of non-printed paper area would be a middletone. As the printing dots become smaller and the non-printing areas larger, the highlight tones are approached. As the printed area becomes greater than 50 percent of the total area, the shadow tones are approached. The screen ruling (coarse or fine) makes no difference in tone values. A tone value of 50 percent in either a 65-line screen or a 150-line screen still looks like a checkerboard — alternating equal-sized squares of printed dots and non-printed spaces. The visible difference due to the screen ruling would not be in the tone value, but in the ability of the naked eye to see the dot structure.

DETERMINING THE SIZE OF SCREEN RULING TO USE. Screens are available in a variety of rulings. There are coarse screens (less than 110 lines to the inch), and there are fine screens (120 lines to the inch or more). The type of work that is to be produced will, to a considerable extent, determine the screen ruling that should be used. At a distance the human eye will not be able to distinguish the individual dots formed by a coarse-line screen even though these dots are relatively far apart. For this reason, large display posters are usually shot with a 25- or 50-line ruling, while work that is to be viewed at normal reading distance will be shot with a screen ruling of 120 or more lines. For ordinary lithographic work of good quality, a 133-line screen is the one most commonly used. However, within the last few years, there has been a definite trend toward the 150-line screen as a standard. The finer the ruling, the greater the detail that can be held in the reproduction. In addition, finer rulings are used for color work due to their ability to minimize the moiré patterns that form.

Paper quality is another factor that determines the screen ruling that is selected. The smoother the paper, the finer the screen that can be printed. For this reason, many jobs are printed today with halftones finer than 150 line. When using a smooth-surface stock, such as a cast-coated sheet, a 250-line screen can produce jobs of exceptionally fine detail. In special types of work, such as the reproduction of aerial photographs, a 300-line screen is used with smooth-surfaced stock to hold a maximum of detail.

The following list shows various screen rulings and where they are generally used in lithography:

Billboard Posters	9 to 50 line
Large Posters	25 to 50 line
Small Display Posters	100 to 133 line
Can Labels.	120 to 133 line
*General Commercial Lithography	120 to 150 line
*Quality Lithography	133 to 250 line

*Selection of screen ruling is based upon the detail in the original art, press equipment, paper, and other factors.

25. FOCUSING WITH A SCREEN IN POSITION

Although a halftone image can be focused with the screen in position, it is not fully satisfactory or convenient. One method of focusing the image is to move the screen into position in front of the ground glass, and then move it as far forward (toward the lens) as the camera will allow. This will throw the screen out of focus and allow you to focus the image without being disturbed by the screen pattern. As the screen is in the optical path, the effect of its thickness is automatically compensated for. When the halftone exposure is to be made, the screen is moved back into its correct position at the proper distance from the sensitive emulsion.

The fault in this method is that the screen blocks about 75 percent of the light that would normally reach the ground glass. This makes it more difficult for the photographer to see the image clearly.

THE GLASS SCREEN COMPENSATOR. When a negative is to be made, the camera is focused so that the image on the ground glass is sharp. However, to shoot a halftone, the glass screen is inserted into the optical path. The extra thickness of the glass of the screen refracts the light so that the focal point is at a slightly greater distance from the lens than would be the case without the screen in position. If the original setting were maintained, the image would be slightly out of focus due to the screen being in the optical path. The compensator is designed to eliminate this problem.

The glass screen compensator is a special piece of glass that is inserted behind the lens and into the optical path of the process camera. It is usually mounted in a pivoting frame directly below the lens. A shaft protrudes through the lensboard allowing the photographer to swing the compensator into the optical path or remove it at will. When preparing to shoot a halftone, the use of a compensator makes it possible to accurately focus the image with the glass screen out of the way. The glass compensator can be of any shape so long as it covers a large enough area to allow all the light rays from the lens to pass through it. In general practice, however, it is usually made in a circular shape.

Figure 19   Glass Screen Compensating Glass

A compensator is made of the same type of glass as the screen itself. It is so designed that it changes or shifts the optical path of the light rays through the lens in exactly the same manner as the glass screen does. This shift of the optical path is known as refraction and is discussed in detail in Chapter XIV, Section 52.

When a glass halftone screen is to be used, the compensator is first swung into position behind the lens. The image is then focused through the compensator onto the ground glass. As the thickness of the compensator glass is the same as the thickness of the halftone screen, it displaces the image so that it comes to a focus at the same point as it would if the screen itself were in position. After focusing, before the shot is made, the compensator is removed and the glass screen is placed into position.

26. COMBINATION LINE AND HALFTONE STOPS

The compensator can also be used when a combination line and halftone shot is to be made. In this case, both the line and halftone shots are made from the one piece of copy. The copy can be a single unit or with overlays for either the line or the halftone parts of the image. It is essential that both the line and the halftone images be recorded with the image equally sharp and of exactly the same size. Focusing one shot with a screen in position and one shot without it would produce two equally sharp images, but they would be of different sizes. If the image were focused for one of these shots (either with the screen or without it) and then the other shot made without refocusing, the second image would be unsharp.

The compensator takes care of this by allowing the operator to shoot the line shots with the compensator in position. Then, with the screen in position and the compensator swung away, the halftone images are shot. When stripped together, both the line and the halftone images will fit.

27. THE THEORY OF THE ACTION OF THE GLASS HALFTONE SCREEN

We take for granted such things as airplanes, automobiles, and television. Although we can use these things, few of us would be able to make one, and still fewer of us would have more than the haziest idea of the theory or theories involved in these devices or their component parts. To a great extent, the same thing is true with the glass halftone screen. As lithographers we may use the screen daily, yet few of us understand the theories that have been proposed as a means of explaining its action. That there are several theories is proof that even the authorities don't agree on the "why's" of screen action.

In general, three main theories have been proposed. These are:

1. The diffraction theory
2. The penumbral theory
3. The pinhole theory

Each of these theories is dependent upon certain properties of light. To more clearly understand the theories of screen action, additional points concerning the properties of light must be considered. (The nature of light is discussed in detail in Chapter XIV, Section 50.)

RECTILINEAR PROPAGATION AND WAVE FRONTS. We usually think of light as traveling from one place to another in a straight line. This concept of travel is known as the rectilinear propagation of light. Propagation, in this sense, means to extend or transmit through space; rectilinear means moving in a straight line.

Another method to describe the way light travels is to consider it as emitting from the source in a wave motion. This concept is the one most commonly accepted by scientists today as most clearly showing the nature of light travel.

Probably the best way to explain wave motion is by recalling something we have all seen. When we throw a stone into a quiet pool of water we create a disturbance that shows itself as little waves which gradually spread out from the point where the stone struck the surface to the edge of the pool.

As the stone enters the water, it immediately comes in contact with surface water particles that it set into motion. As these water particles move, they act on the particles next to them and set them into motion. These particles, in turn, move the particles alongside of them, and gradually all of the surface water particles in the pool are disturbed. None of the particles move any great distance, yet the disturbance created moves through the entire pool as waves. As we have pictured it here, each point (or particle) on the wave front may be considered as the source of a new series of waves. This concept is known as Huygens' Principle. It has very far-reaching application to us when we consider the diffraction theory of screen action.

28. DIFFRACTION

Diffraction is the apparent bending of light around the edges of an obstacle that is put in its path. At first glance this seems impossible, for if we consider that light travels in a straight line, then any obstacle that blocked the path of light rays would stop them and not allow any to get behind the obstacle. However, if we consider that light travels by means of a wave motion, then the conception of diffraction is logically explained.

Let us study Figure 20 to more clearly understand how diffraction works. Picture a wave front approaching a barrier AC. The barrier has a very small opening in it at B. The portion of the wave that strikes the barrier at any place except the opening is absorbed or reflected back in the direction from which it came. However, the portion of the wave that strikes the opening will go through and, if the opening is

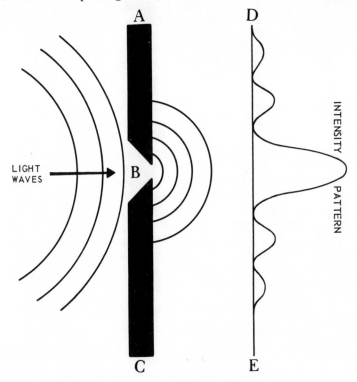

Figure 20   Diffraction Theory of Dot Formation

small enough, it will act as the source of a new series of waves. In this way the new series of waves will actually illuminate the back of the obstacle.

If these new light waves, produced at B, continue until they strike a photographic plate (DE) they will produce an intensity pattern similar to the one shown at the right of DE. This pattern shows that the light coming in a direct line through the center of the opening will expose the plate to the greatest extent at the point known as the central maximum. The pattern also shows that the illumination will fall off as we go to either side of this point. This could, in a photographic plate, produce a dark, heavily exposed center area that gradually fades off as we move away from the center. This, as you can see, illustrates Huygens' Principle. At the same time it gives us our first glimpse of the diffraction theory.

Diffraction is a difficult phenomenon to understand. Perhaps this is because we usually think of light as traveling in straight lines and, therefore, diffraction seems to be some kind of aberration of light under certain conditions. Actually, ". . . diffraction is a fundamental property of light, and rectilinear propagation is merely a special case occurring when the wave front is unrestricted."[1]

28A. The Diffraction Theory. The first of the theories listed in Section 27 — the diffraction theory — is the one that is most widely accepted by serious research workers in the field. Its application to halftone dot formation was first suggested by Max Levy in 1896[2]. It was later elaborated by Fruwirth and Mertle[3]. Additional studies of the phenomenon have been made by Yule[4] and Harrison[5]. The theory proposes that each of the openings in the halftone screen acts as an imperfect lens to project an image on the plate. The object of this image is the lens diaphragm of the camera. However, because the screen opening acts as an imperfect lens, the image that is formed is also imperfect and accounts for the fringe area around the dot that is formed.

(1) A. C. Hardy and F. H. Perrin, *The Principles of Optics,* McGraw-Hill Book Company, New York, 1932, p. 124.

(2) M. Levy, *Process Photogram,* 3:20, 1896.

(3) A. Fruwirth and J. S. Mertle, *Diffraction Theory of Halftone,* International Photo-Engravers Union of North America, 1936.

(4) J. A. C. Yule, J. Franklin Institute, 235 (5), 483, 1943.

(5) V. G. W. Harrison, "The Theory of the Halftone Screen: A study in Diffraction," *Photographic Journal,* 92B: 74, 1952.

The fringe area can be explained in this manner. A cross-sectional view of a halftone dot resembles a mountain with sloped sides. The central portion of this dot-mountain consists of an area that has had sufficient exposure and development to create the visual appearance of a black tone. This is due to the amount of silver grains that have been developed and their light-blocking ability when viewed by light transmitted through the image.

The side slopes, however, have had only a portion of the silver grains sufficiently exposed for development. This area gives the visual appearance of a gray tone and looks like a gray fringe around the darker central portion of the dot. This sloped area is known as the fringe area of the dot.

Applying these concepts, a square diaphragm in the original camera lens system will create a square dot on the final plate. A round diaphragm will create a round dot. In addition, each glass crossline screen was assumed to have a focal length. In order to produce the sharpest dot possible, the screen should be set at this proper distance. The focal length (F.L.) of the screen is determined by the formula:

$$\text{F.L.} = \frac{d^2}{3\lambda}$$

This is according to the calculations of Fruwirth and Mertle. In this formula:

F.L. = focal length of the screen
d = length of one side of the screen opening
λ = wavelength of the light

Using this data a reasonably complete system of screen distances, lens stops, etc. were worked out. However, the

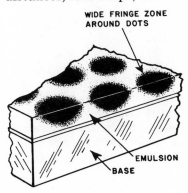

WIDE FRINGE ZONE
AROUND DOTS

EMULSION

BASE

Figure 21 Halftone Dots Exposed Through Screen

screen has its "lenses" very close together and, because of diffraction, interference takes place. The combined effect of diffraction and interference must be considered. This is due to the fact that we must consider light as traveling in a wave motion rather than in the straight-line movement of a stream of particles or corpuscles. Perhaps this is best explained by Edwin Schrödinger, who said:

"We consider a small, almost point-like source which emits corpuscles in all directions, and a screen with two small holes, with shutters, so that we can open first only the one, then only the other, then both. Behind the screen we have a photographic plate which collects the corpuscles that emerge from the openings. After the plate has been developed, it shows, let me assume, the marks of the single corpuscles that have hit it, each rendering a grain of silver-bromide developable, so that it shows a black speck after developing.

"Now let us first open only one hole. You might expect that after exposing for some time we get a close cluster around one spot. This is not so. Apparently the particles are deflected from their straight path at the opening. You get a fairly wide spreading of black specks, though they are densest in the middle, becoming rarer at greater angles. If you open the second hole alone, you clearly get a similar pattern, only around a different center.

"Now let us open both holes at the same time and expose the plate just as long as before. What would you expect — if the idea was correct, the single individual particles fly from the source to one of the holes, are deflected there, then continue along another straight line until they are caught by the plate? Clearly you would expect to get the two former patterns superimposed.

"Thus in the region where the two fans overlap, if near a given point of the pattern you had, say 25 spots per unit area in the first experiment, and 16 more in the second, you would expect to find $25 + 16 = 41$ in the third experiment. This is not so. Keeping to these numbers (and disregarding chance fluctuations, for the sake of argument), you may find anything between 81 spots and only 1 spot[1], this depending upon the precise place on the plate. It is decided by the difference of its distance from the holes. The result is that in the overlapping part we get dark fringes separated by fringes of scarcity.

---

(1) The numbers 1 and 81 are obtained as $(\sqrt{25} \pm \sqrt{16})^2 = (5 \pm 4)^2 = 81,1$.

"If one wanted to keep up the idea of single individual particles flying continuously and independently either through one or through the other slit one would have to assume something quite ridiculous, namely that in some places on the plate the particles destroy each other to a large extent, while at other places they 'produce offspring.' This is not only ridiculous but can be refuted by experiment. (Making the source extremely weak and exposing for a very long time. This does not change the pattern.) The only other alternative is to assume that a particle flying through the opening number 1 is influenced also by the opening number 2, and that in an extremely mysterious fashion."[1]

28B. Comments on the Diffraction Theory. In his comments on the diffraction theory, Harrison[2] states that the fact that the halftone dot is *not* an image of the diaphragm can be proved experimentally. As an example, he says that using a stop with a square aperture, and having the sides of this square parallel to the screen rulings, the halftone dot that is formed in the middletone areas is actually of a square shape when the screen distance is correct, but (and here is the big factor) the "image" is oriented at an angle of 45° to the diaphragm. When the same square aperture is rotated through a 45° arc into normal working position, there are minor differences in the dot shape, but *the orientation of the squares in the middletones is unaffected.*

In addition Harrison states, "The shapes of the halftone dots are fundamentally the same whether the diaphragm be round or square, and whatever be the orientation of this square. Moreover, by suitable adjustment of screen distance, round stops may be made to give square dots and square stops round dots. These simple observations appear to have escaped notice in the literature."[3]

Another comment on the early diffraction theory was that the size of the dot could not be made below a certain limit as determined by the size of the stop used. This, in the light of present considerations of the diffraction theory, seems to be in error.

---

(1) E. Schrödinger, "Causality and Wave Mechanics," *The World of Mathematics,* V. 2, Simon and Schuster, New York, 1956.
(2) V. G. W. Harrison, "The Theory of the Halftone Screen: A Study in Diffraction," *Photographic Journal,* 92B: 74, 1952.
(3) Harrison, *op. cit.,* p. 76.

28C. Conclusions on the Diffraction Theory. The following additional conclusions have been proposed at one time or another by those who support the diffraction theory:

1. Every screen has a definite speed ratio, the finer lined screens having the greatest speed. This speed is in ratio to the squares of the screen apertures. Thus, a 100-line screen has only one-fourth the speed of a 200-line screen.

2. The proper screen distance for a screen varies with each change in camera extension, just as the camera bellows extension varies with each change in copyboard distance. However, because of the extremely short focal length of the screen, it is not necessary to vary the screen distance but to vary the camera lens aperture in proportion.

3. Although the screen is similar to a lens in many of the ways that it operates, it does not have correction for color aberrations the way a quality lens would have. Thus, with varying filters or varying wavelengths of light, the screen distance should be varied.

29. THE PENUMBRAL THEORY

This theory of screen action was originally proposed by Dolland and Tallent[1], and still later by Deville[2]. In the early 1900's it was further expounded by Clerc and Calmels[3]. Their basic theory is described as follows: When the light from a relatively large light source strikes a smaller opaque object, the shadow that is cast behind the opaque object has two areas — one of total darkness called the *umbra,* and one of partial darkness which is called the *penumbra.* The eclipses of the sun and the moon show how these areas of umbra and penumbra are formed by natural bodies.

The penumbral theory proposes that the lens diaphragm acts in a manner similar to the sun. The opaque areas of the halftone screen block the light from the diaphragm in much the same manner as the earth blocks the sun's light. In forming the halftone dot structure, the proponents of this theory believe the dot is due to illuminated and partially illuminated (penumbral) areas, and this accounts for the shoulder areas of the halftone dots.

---

(1) A. W. Dolland and A. K. Tallent, *Photographic Journal,* 1895, 35:273-284.
(2) E. E. Deville, *Process Photogram,* 1896, 3:136.
(3) L. P. Clerc, *La Technique des Reproductions Photomechaniques,* Bouzard-Calmels, 1948, 104-116.

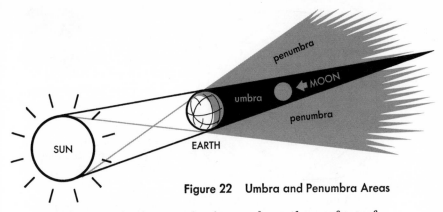

Figure 22   Umbra and Penumbra Areas

If we were of microscopic size, and on the surface of a photographic emulsion looking toward the lens aperture during a period of exposure, we would see that portions of the aperture would be eclipsed due to the position of the screen and our own position. The intensity of the light that would be falling upon us would be in proportion to the amount of aperture that we could observe. If we then moved to different positions on the surface of the emulsion and made measurements of the intensity of the light at these various points, we could connect points of equal intensity and in this way get a "map" of the surface of the emulsion. Such a map has already been made by Yule[1], where he connected points of equal intensity with lines to form contours known as isolux lines. On diagrams of this type it is usual to superimpose both the screen and the lens apertures. Figure 25 illustrates such a graphic representation of dot formation.

(1) J. A. C. Yule, *The Theory of the Halftone Process,* J. Franklin Institute, 231:23-28, 1941; 235:438-498, 1943.

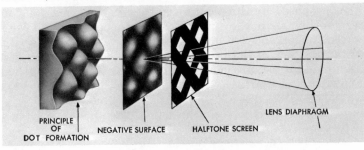

PRINCIPLE OF DOT FORMATION   NEGATIVE SURFACE   HALFTONE SCREEN   LENS DIAPHRAGM

Figure 23   Halftone Dot Formation by the Penumbral Theory

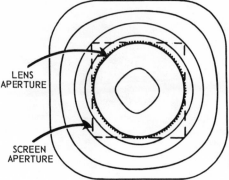

LENS
APERTURE

SCREEN
APERTURE

Figure 24   Eclipse
by Screen Ruling

Figure 25   Isolux Diagram Showing Dot Formation According to the Penumbral Theory

Although not as acceptable to the serious workers as the diffraction theory, it has been found that in practice the penumbral theory offers a good approximation of actual values.

29A. Glass Screen Operation as Explained by the Penumbral Theory. According to the penumbral theory, the actual operation of the glass halftone screen is based upon the mathematical relationship that exists among four factors. These factors are screen aperture, lens aperture, screen distance, and camera extension. They are related to each other according to the following formula:

$$\frac{\text{screen aperture}}{\text{screen distance}} = \frac{\text{lens aperture}}{\text{camera extension}}$$

Using this formula you will note that the screen can be placed at any distance from the emulsion provided the lens aperture is changed by the appropriate amount to allow the formula to balance. This is in contradiction to the diffraction theory which maintains that a screen has a definite focal length and, therefore, the screen distance should be fixed.

As proposed by the penumbral theory, the same dot pattern (other than the linear scale) can be produced with screens of 100 and 200 lines provided that the proper screen distance is set for both of these screens. This, however, has been found to be untrue experimentally, and writers such as Fruwirth and Mertle[1], Grenell[2], Tritton[3], and Hislop[4] have

(1) A. Fruwirth and J. S. Mertle, *Diffraction Theory of Halftone,* International Photo-Engravers Union of North America, 1936.

(2) R. Grenell, *Penrose Annual,* 1922, 24, 65.

(3) F. J. Tritton, *Photographic Journal,* 81:235, 1941.

(4) W. J. C. Hislop, *Process Engravers Monthly,* 56:73, 1949.

maintained that the correct screen distance cannot be calculated by the previous formula. They suggest that for coarse line screens the distance should be greater than that calculated, while for fine line screens the distance should be less. Yule[1] noted that when abnormally short screen distances and coarse-lined screens were used, both the calculated and actual results agreed in general with the penumbral theory calculations. Here diffraction plays a minor role. However, when fine line screens and normal screen distances were used, there were very wide discrepancies between the calculated and actual results. This can only be explained as the effects of diffraction.

LTF studies of halftone methods, carried out for the U. S. Air Force, have shown that glass screen resolution quality is at its best with the techniques that minimize diffraction scattering of image detail while producing good dot structure. Close screen distances and large lens stops favor this. A f ratio of 32 is recommended rather than 64. Image sharpness may be almost doubled and exposures cut to one-fourth. The long screen distances and small stops, which have been recommended for too long a time, are a hangover from wet plate photography which is now practically obsolete.

29B. Lens Aperture and Camera Extension Ratios by Penumbral Theory. With the majority of practical work being done on the basis of the penumbral theory, certain relationships have been suggested as being the most satisfactory. The penumbral equation shows on the right side of the "equal sign" a relationship between the lens aperture and the camera extension. The two most common relationships or ratios are the 1:45 ratio, and the 1:64 ratio. In other words, the diameter of the lens aperture (in the 1:64 ratio) will be 1/64 of the camera extension. If, therefore, the camera extension were 32″, then the lens aperture would be 1/64 of that amount or 1/2″.

29C. Lens Aperture and Dot Size by the Penumbral Theory. Many photographers find that when a certain lens aperture is maintained they obtain what they consider to be the best dot. It is generally accepted in the trade that the aperture has an effect upon the dot structure when using the glass screen. But most photographers have only a hazy idea, if

(1) J. A. C. Yule, *The Theory of the Halftone Process,* J. Franklin Institute, 231:23-28, 1941; 235:438-498, 1943.

any, of exactly what this effect is. Let us look, therefore, at what happens to the dot when the aperture is changed. The following diagram is based upon the penumbral theory of halftone dot formation and is the basis of our explanation.

Let us first assume a given aperture width and then see how the dot is formed and what its structure is. From that starting point we will vary the aperture and note what happens to the resulting dot.

Light entering the aperture is limited by the edges of the aperture. You will note that from these edges lines have been drawn to fall upon the edges of the lines of the halftone screen. These lines are further continued until they strike the surface of the sensitive emulsion (see Figure 26).

The light passes through the clear areas of the halftone screen with no interference from the black lines of the screen. However, due to the position of the lens aperture and the openings of the screen (the screen apertures), a certain angular relationship exists. This is determined by four factors: 1) The width of the lens aperture; 2) The distance from the lens aperture to the screen aperture; 3) The width of the screen aperture; and 4) The distance from the screen aperture to the light-sensitive emulsion.

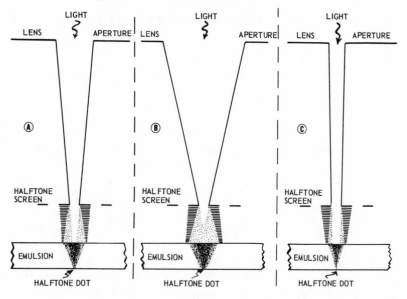

Figure 26   Relationship of Lens Aperture and Dot Size Structure

With the relationship shown in Figure 26(A), you will note that the edges of the lens aperture cast shadows behind the black lines. These shadows create areas of partial illumination behind the screen apertures which are then projected on the surface of the emulsion. This light of varying intensity — being brighter in the center area of projection and gradually fading away toward the edges — is the light that creates the halftone dot in the light-sensitive emulsion. Being more fully exposed in the center, the halftone dot develops a core whose density is greater than the density at the edges. This, then, is how the dot is formed and explains the part played by the lens aperture in its formation.

Now let us take a second condition — one in which nothing is changed except that the lens aperture is made larger. Figure 26(B) illustrates this. With this condition, the angle of spread of the light rays is greater. Therefore, under this condition, a larger area of the sensitive emulsion is affected, and the dot area becomes larger.

With a smaller opening than our original example, Figure 26(C), the area of the spread of the dot becomes smaller, and a smaller dot is formed. Thus, by the use of this simple geometric construction we are able to see how the larger lens aperture will create a larger dot than a smaller aperture, all other things being held constant.

30. LENS STOPS

Within the elements of the process lens, there is a diaphragm integrally built into the lens barrel to control the size of the opening or aperture. The purpose of this diaphragm is to limit the beams of light that will pass through the optical system. There is also some means of temporarily inserting an auxiliary device that will give a smaller or differently shaped aperture than that produced by the diaphragm. This auxiliary device is called a lens stop. Since an image of the aperture is projected through the optical system, the shape of the aperture can help to determine the final shape of the image that is projected onto the sensitive emulsion. Thus, when used with the glass crossline screen, a round aperture can create a round dot, while a rectangular aperture can create a rectangular dot shape on the sensitive emulsion. In addition to these two simple shapes, stops of many other shapes have been proposed for use with the crossline screen. Each has had its purpose, and the proponent of each shape has loudly proclaimed its advantages over the then existing stops. There are far too many lens stop shapes to mention all of them, but a few are described in the following pages. We have limited the number of these descriptions because some of the proposals are extremely complex and not important enough to devote time to them here.

30A. The Iris Diaphragm. This is the most common diaphragm in use today. It is found on almost any modern lens that is constructed with a diaphragm as an integral part of the lens assembly. The iris diaphragm consists of a number of thin blades (usually of steel) that are fastened through a hinging arrangement to a control ring or lever. As this ring is turned the blades fan out, reducing the size of the opening through which light can pass. The device is so designed that the opening maintains its circular shape regardless of its diameter. The outer control ring is usually found on the lens barrel approximately halfway between the ends. It is usually calibrated for the standard U. S. diaphragm openings such as f9, f11, f16, f22, etc.

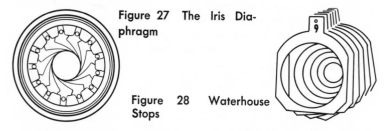

Figure 27   The Iris Diaphragm

Figure   28   Waterhouse Stops

30B. The Waterhouse Stop. The Waterhouse stop is a diaphragm that consists of a thin metal plate with a circular opening in it. It is inserted into the lens barrel between the lens elements. For this purpose, the lens barrel usually has a slot into which the stop can be inserted. When Waterhouse stops are supplied for a lens, they usually come in a set of varying size apertures. The most common use of this stop today is for the purpose of "flashing."[1] Flashing is an overall exposure on the negative through a small lens stop that creates a tiny dot.

Waterhouse stops are supplied with most process lenses. They are provided even with lenses which have a built-in diaphragm. The reason for this is that the iris diaphragm is

(1) This technique was described in detail in Chapter VI.

mechanically limited by its construction as to the smallest size aperture it can make. For the purpose of flashing, this smallest aperture may not be small enough, and so a Waterhouse stop with a very small opening is provided. The apertures of all Waterhouse stops and the iris diaphragm must be in line with the lens axis, otherwise an irregular dot shape will be produced when working with a combination exposure technique.

30C. The Square Stop. The previously discussed stops have one factor in common. Both the iris diaphragm and the Waterhouse stop have circular apertures. This is the standard shape and most widely used today. However, many researchers at various times in the history of halftone photography felt that the round stop was not the complete answer to good dot structure and quality. The square stop was, therefore, proposed as a substitute for the round stop, or at least as an adjunct to it to improve quality. This square shape was felt to be especially useful when copying black-and-white subjects of a low contrast. The claim is that the square stop closes up the highlight areas of the negative better, gives generally improved dot formation, and requires a shorter exposure. In closing up these highlight areas in a more efficient manner, the contrast of the negative is increased. This is of advantage when shooting from flat originals. Other photographers feel that the value of the square aperture is minimized by the nuisance of its handling compared with the ease of using the built-in iris diaphragm. The point is still not settled, but in almost every area you will find some workers who highly praise the square aperture.

In the event you decide to experiment with the square stop, bear in mind that the size of each stop must be equivalent to a corresponding round aperture. To find the length of a side of the square stop, that is equivalent to a specific round aperture, multiply the diameter of the round aperture by 0.886. This will give you the required length of the side of the square for construction purposes. In addition, when using a square stop, the diagonal of the square should be set parallel to the ruling of the glass screen.

30D. The Dog-Eared Stop.[1] The dog-eared stop consists of a square opening with additional small triangular shaped open-

(1) G. W. Jorgensen, "Dog-Eared Stop Cuts Halftone Exposure Time," *LTF Research Progress,* 21:3, 4, April 1951.

Figure 29   The Dog-Eared Stop

ings extending outward from each corner of the original square. These added openings are the "dog-ears" that give the stop its name.

The purpose of the dog-eared stop, as is the case with many of the special stops that have been proposed, is to improve the quality of the 50 percent dot. When a 50 percent dot is made through round apertures, it is difficult to produce a perfect square-shaped dot. The pin-cushion or barrel shapes which result are more difficult to judge than the true checkerboard pattern that is formed by a perfect 50 percent opaque dot. In addition, the 50 percent tone value is more difficult to maintain on the press. The dog-ears add additional exposure to the corner portions of the 50 percent dot, thus extending its corner area and producing a more nearly square 50 percent dot.

In use, the dog-eared stop is inserted into the slot in the lens barrel. The stop is aligned in such a way that the square sides of the opening are vertical and at a 45° angle to the ruling of the halftone screen. This means that the dog-ears diagonally opposite each other will be aligned with the ruling of the screen. This results because the dog-ears are cut at a 45° angle to the square sides.

The dog-eared stop is never used as the only stop in an exposure. It is used for only a portion of the exposure time. When shooting halftones using a two- or three-stop exposure system, the dog-eared stop is substituted for the highlight stop. With a one-stop system, the regular stop is used for a portion of the exposure, then opened or removed, and the remainder of the exposure is made with the dog-eared stop. This will become clearer when you read the sections in Chapter IX pertaining to multiple stops.

When inserted in the lens barrel, the dog-eared stop must be the only determining factor in the size and shape of the aperture. For this reason, the iris diaphragm that is found on modern lenses should be opened to its widest aperture so that it doesn't interfere with the action of the stop.

MAKING THE DOG-EARED STOP. A dog-eared stop has the shape shown in Figure 29. The diagram is "same-size" and can be used as a pattern to make your own stops. For a 19″ lens its area corresponds roughly to a round stop of about f24. A somewhat larger size hole may be desirable for lenses having longer focal lengths.

At the LTF lab, the stops were cut out of process film that was blackened and made opaque by exposure to light and development. The "dog-eared" hole was trimmed out with a razor blade. Any other opaque material can also be used to make the stop but will probably be more difficult to cut.

Figure 29 shows the correct position of the aperture for use with a glass screen set at 45°. The square sides of the aperture must always be at a 45° angle to the screen rulings. Separate stops should thus be made for each screen angle used in multicolor work.

HOW TO USE THE DOG-EARED STOP. If you are using a three-stop halftone exposure system, substitute the dog-eared stop for your present middletone stop. If a two-stop system is being used, substitute the dog-eared stop for the highlight stop. If a one-stop system is being used, reduce the exposure time through the single stop and add a second short exposure through the dog-eared stop.

One size dog-eared stop can be used for magnifications that range from about one-half size to twice size. For work outside this range either the size of the stop or the screen distance should be adjusted as per usual procedure. The size of the other round stops used in the multiple-stop system should be changed as usual according to the magnification ratio.

When shooting two-stop halftones, the exposure ratio between the round stop and the dog-eared stop should be varied according to the contrast of the copy as with usual practice.

SCREEN DISTANCE WITH THE DOG-EARED STOP. Screen distance becomes more and more critical as the size of an aperture increases. You will notice that the dog-eared stop is larger than the highlight stops ordinarily used. Therefore, when the dog-eared stop is used, the screen distance becomes more critical. It should be set carefully to obtain maximum resolution and the best possible dot quality.

In order to avoid the odd shaped diffraction patterns that signal incorrect screen distance, the following procedure is suggested:

If you are using a 133-line screen, one of the best screen distances using ortho film will be close to 12/64 inch measured from the cover glass. Shoot three halftones of a gray scale using the dog-eared stop during part of the exposure. Expose one at 12/64, one at 11/64, and one at 13/64. Examine each halftone with a magnifier using dark field illumination to determine the best image. A description of dark field illumination is found in Chapter VII, Section 18A.

30E. Special Stops and Stop Controls. In addition to those previously mentioned, many additional stops have been proposed for use in making halftone exposures. Still others have been suggested for special photographic operations that use a halftone screen.

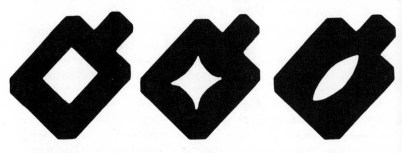

Figure 30   Various Stops

CONSTANT-MOVEMENT DIAPHRAGMS. To eliminate the necessity of using various apertures during exposure with a multiple-stop system, a special diaphragm mechanism is available. This is connected to the diaphragm control and is in constant movement during the exposure so as to be continually changing the aperture.[1]

FILTER STOPS. To achieve the same effect as a multiple-stop exposure, a stop was proposed by F. E. Ives many years ago. It consisted of a diaphragm made of a sheet of optically flat glass with parallel sides covered with a sheet of yellow-filter material having a small hole cut out of its center. In addition, an opaque border was provided that determines the

_____

(1) A. Brandweiner, British Patent No. 17581, 1900.

final size of the opening. The difference in aperture area through the clear and yellow portions of the opening, plus the exposure differential, gave the effect of a multiple-stop exposure.

STAR-SHAPED STOPS. Another type of aperture that has been suggested is a star-shaped diaphragm opening. Many variations on this basic pattern have been proposed, usually by varying the number of star points.

LINE STOPS. In addition to the apertures that have been suggested for ordinary halftone work, special stops have been designed for particular purposes. One example of this can be seen in the production of screen tints.

It may be necessary at times to produce a tint of straight parallel lines rather than the usual one of halftone dots. One advantage of such a tint is that it is easier to run on the press than a dot tint. For this purpose, a stop can be made that consists of a straight line opening that will run as close to the optical axis (exact center) of the lens as is possible. The entire exposure is made through this aperture. The straight-line opening of the stop must be aligned in such a manner as to be parallel to the angle of the screen ruling[1]. Such an aperture has even been proposed for use without a lens, and taped onto the lensboard in the position normally occupied by the lens.[2]

SMALL STOPS FOR SMALL DOTS. The general supposition in the trade is that the use of a smaller stop for flashing will produce a smaller dot in the shadow areas of the negative. This factor is discounted by Harrison[3] who maintains that dots will not be smaller with smaller stops if the exposures are strictly equivalent. By this he means that identical dots would be formed provided that the exposures given would be strictly equivalent. In other words the exposures must be adjusted so that the intensity of the illumination will be identical at the central maximum. This was described in Section 28C when discussing diffraction. In actual practice, however, the control permitted by the usual process camera, and the time allotted for careful calculation and measurement

(1) *Army Map Service Bulletin* #12, October 1944, page 18.

(2) *Process Negative Making With the Douthitt Diaphragm Control System,* The Douthitt Corporation, Detroit, Michigan, page 28.

(3) V. G. W. Harrison, "The Theory of the Halftone Screen: A Study in Diffraction," *Photographic Journal,* 92B:74, 1952.

during the normal workload, are not enough to assure that identical central maximums of intensity can be obtained. For this reason, the photographer will soon find that, as a practical measure, the use of a smaller diaphragm opening will produce a smaller dot. However, if the aperture is exceedingly small, then the quality of the shadow dot will become poorer and more ragged in shape due to excess diffraction. Diffraction effects take over from penumbra shadows when using small apertures. Prolonged exposures, required by extremely small apertures, make it possible for dust particles in the air to diffract some of the reflected light to the lens, as well as that from the lens to the film. This gives rise to poor dot shapes. Minute vibration of the camera also contributes to poor dot shape when exposures are too long.

When multiple stops are used to make an exposure, a typical exposure would consist of the main exposure made on the basis of the 1:45 ratio, while the supplementary exposure, used to create the finer dots, is made on the 1:64 ratio. The idea behind this multiple exposure is that it improved the gradation of the negative. However, a great deal of recent research has been done to see if multiple stops improve the gradation of the negatives or positives. There seems to be no actual evidence that improved gradation can be expected from varying either the size or the shape of the diaphragm.

31. THE PINHOLE THEORY

This theory was proposed in 1878 by F. E. Ives. He stated that each opening of the crossline screen was the equivalent of a pinhole lens, and that these apertures of the screen were each actually forming a vignetted image of the lens aperture onto the negative that was being made. Ives believed that only a tiny pinpoint of light was projected through the apertures that photographed the darker areas of the copy, and the whiter areas of the copy produced a larger dot by reflecting more light.

32. CONCLUSIONS ON GLASS HALFTONE SCREEN THEORY

At this point you might well be saying, "Okay, there are a lot of theories, but which one is right?" There is no definite answer to this question. The modern consensus on the subject seems to be that the diffraction theory is necessary to complete the description of the action of the glass halftone screen in forming the halftone dot. The penumbral theory has been kept alive because it offers a fairly close approximation and, in practice, the penumbral theory equation discussed in Section 29A is usable and useful.

However, here is additional material that is relevant. The majority of cameramen appear to be basically unfamiliar with any of these theories. However, most of them have adopted what could be called a system based upon a modified version of the penumbral theory. It is surprising that with so many varied methods of working they still manage to turn out acceptable halftones. What, then, must the screen be producing in the way of dots, to be acceptable under such a wide variety of operating methods?

To answer this we must consider the buyer of lithography, and how his demands influence the type of halftone that is produced. The basic request seems to be, "I want snap in the picture, but don't lose the fine tones."

The most important part of this statement is that the buyer wants "snap" or contrast in the picture. He considers a good printed reproduction to be one that has the black areas of the picture as black as possible, the light areas almost white, and the in-between values holding the detail.

This means that the halftone negative should have a non-printing dot in the darkest shadow areas of the negative, the middletones should be about correct, and the highlight areas of the negative should be almost completely closed up. The result is a serious loss of quarter-tone gradations and produces such things as chalky faces, etc. Even though the negative is distorted and does not have the tonal characteristics of the original, it is satisfactory to many viewers.

Many will not agree with this despite the large number of buyers of lithography who prefer this type of product rather than a truer rendition of the tonal values of the original. This could be a reason why so many variations in techniques, in different plants, produce commercially satisfactory halftone images even though they do not follow any of the "theories" of so-called "best reproduction."

Chapter IX

SHOOTING HALFTONES WITH THE GLASS SCREEN

In Chapter VIII, "Principles of the Glass Halftone Screen," several theories of how the screen affects dot formation and structure were discussed. A fact common to the three theories discussed is that each opening in the screen does act as an aperture through which light passes to cause an exposure on the film behind each opening in the screen. Figure 26 demonstrated the effect of changing the size of the lens aperture on dot structure. Figure 31 shows that if the lens aperture is held constant, moving the screen closer or away from the film will produce the same effect. The character of the dot is to some extent dependent upon the size of the aperture used. Many photographers use partial exposures through different size stops to build the dot structure they desire.

33. FOCUSING THE SCREEN

When a photographer starts to work with the glass halftone screen, he soon learns that it must be kept at a certain distance from the sensitive emulsion in order to obtain a good dot. Most halftone photographers are unfamiliar with the reasons why one distance might be better than another, and why such emphasis is placed upon obtaining the proper screen distance.

The importance of screen distance to the halftone photographer can be summed up in five words ... good dots and tone reproduction! Each opening of the halftone screen is like a small lens and, like a lens, this opening must be kept at a specified distance so that the light passing through the opening comes to a focus at the surface of the sensitive emulsion to create a good dot. This is admittedly not the complete answer to the questions of what happens and why, so let us get a more detailed view of this problem of screen distances.

34. SCREEN RULING AND THE WAVELENGTH OF LIGHT

The screen's ruling is the first factor upon which the screen distance depends. The light passing through the opening in the halftone screen is diffracted at the edges of this opening. The diffraction patterns that form have a bright central band and bands of lesser intensity on each side.

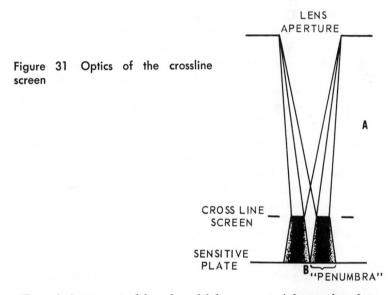

Figure 31 Optics of the crossline screen

These bright central bands, which cross at right angles, form the core of the dot. We can consider the dot as being formed by the rays of light leaving the edges of the screen ruling which cross each other at a certain angle. Therefore, once the angle of the rays of light is known, it sets the distance from the edges at which they will cross and create this bright spot. The distance between the two edges of such a screen opening is, therefore, a deciding factor in determining the angle.

We stated previously that this is only one of the factors involved. The angle is also determined by the wavelength of the light that passes through the opening. Basically, blue light creates the smallest angle, while red light (at the opposite end of the visible spectrum) creates the largest angle. This means that the screen should be further away from the emulsion with blue light than with red to create the same-size dot.

The calculation of screen distance, when the two factors of wavelength and screen aperture are considered, can be made with the following formula:[1]

$$d^2$$

$$D = \frac{d^2}{3 \; \lambda}$$

where D = screen distance
d = screen aperture (diagonal)
λ = wavelength of light

An example using the above formula for a 133-line screen and with light having a wavelength of 460 mu would then have these values:

$$D = \frac{(.096)^2}{3 \times .000460} = 6.6 \text{ mm or } 17/64 \text{ inch.}$$

In the event that the screen was unevenly or inaccurately ruled, a calculation such as this may not be quite accurate.

Although not done in actual practice, when plates or films of different color sensitivity are used for making halftone exposures, the screen distance will vary depending upon the color sensitivity of the emulsion, all else remaining constant. An example of this would be the setting for the same 133-line screen when color-blind emulsions (wavelength 460 mu), ortho emulsions (wavelength 520 mu), and panchromatic emulsions (wavelength 640 mu) are used. In these cases the screen distances would be:

Color-blind .... 17/64″
Orthochromatic .... 15/64″
Panchromatic .... 12/64″

35. SCREEN APERTURE TO SCREEN DISTANCE RATIOS

A practice in common use today is the establishment of the proper screen distance by using a ratio of the screen opening to the screen distance. The ratios most commonly used are 1:32, 1:45, and 1:64. These ratios are easy to use and are sufficiently accurate to provide a simple means of determining screen distance.

(1) Formula and example taken from: B. E. Tory, "Photolithography," *Graphic Arts Monthly,* Chicago, Illinois, 1953, page 61.

Thus, with a 133-line screen, the width of the screen opening would be 1/266 of an inch, and the screen distance would be 32, 45, or 64 times that amount. Using the 1/64 ratio the screen distance would be equal to 64/266 of an inch. This is .241 inch when presented as a decimal, and when converted to the nearest 64th of an inch we get 15/64[1].

Table IV shows the screen distance to the nearest 64th of an inch for various screen rulings and utilizing the 1:32, 1:45, and 1:64 ratios.

Table IV

SCREEN DISTANCES FOR VARIOUS SCREEN RULINGS

RULING LINES PER INCH	1:32 RATIO	1:45 RATIO	SCREEN DISTANCE (64THS) 1:64 RATIO
100	10	14	20
120	9	12	17
133	8	11	15
150	7	10	14
175	6	8	12
200	5	7	10

36. SETTING THE SCREEN

Once the correct screen distance has been determined, the next step is to make the actual screen setting. This is usually done in one of three different ways: 1) With a calibrated wedge; 2) By visual focusing; or 3) By a test exposure.

36A. Setting the Screen With a Calibrated Wedge. The calibrated wedge is exactly what the name implies ... a wedge that has been calibrated for various thicknesses, usually in 64ths of an inch. The procedure for its use is as follows:

(1) These figures are based upon measurement from the ruling of the screen itself, and do not take into account the thickness of the cover glass of the screen. In most cases this cover glass thickness is scratched into the binding edge of the screen. This dimension is included in the distances as calculated above. When setting the screen at its proper distance, 15/64 for example, the actual distance between emulsion plane and the glass surface facing it would measure 15/64" less 2/3 of the cover glass thickness marked on the binding edge of the screen. This is due to the fact that not only are we concerned with the thickness of the glass but also the effective length of the light path through the glass. This light path is longer than it would be through the same thickness of air space.

Figure 32   Aligning the Screen
and Setting Screen Distance

Put a plate into the plate holder on the camera back.

Move the screen into position.

Place the wedge between one corner of the plate and the surface of the screen. Read the value of this spacing on the wedge.

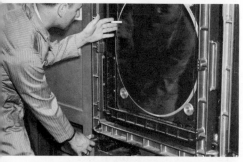

Repeat this step for the remaining three corners of the screen.

If all four corners of the screen read the same on the wedge, move the screen as far forward as you can. Then reposition it and re-check the separation.

If the four corners do not check to the same reading, adjust the alignment screws on the screen mechanism, until the four corners are spaced equally.

Use the screen separation mechanism to move the screen into the proper position.

When setting the proper screen distance with the wedge, it is important that you do not attempt to set one corner accurately and then try to set each of the other corners completely unless the variation between corners is less than 1/32 of an inch. If the discrepancy between readings is greater than 1/32 of an inch, it is best to adjust each corner gradually, moving constantly from corner to corner and making only a slight adjustment at a time.

Caution: The screw adjustments on the screen are used to align the four corners of the screen to equal separations. The final separation is done with the lever mechanism that moves the entire screen into position. The screw adjustments have only limited play. If you attempt to make a large separation with them alone, the screws may drop out, which would, of course, allow the screen to fall.

36B. Screen Setting by Visual Focusing. Using a visual focusing method, it is simple to set the entire screen to the correct screen distance. However, it is extremely difficult to line up the four corners of the screen so that they are at an equal distance from the glass plate that is being used as a guide. Most photographers who use the visual method for setting the screen at the proper distance first use the wedge to align the four corners of the screen.

Various methods have been suggested, over the years, for visual focusing of the halftone screen. Two of the most familiar methods were suggested by Horgan and Turati. A more recent technique has been suggested by Hislop.

Horgan's Method of Visual Focusing. A simple method of visual focusing was suggested by S. H. Horgan. In his method, a grease pencil line is made on a clear glass plate. The plate is placed in the plate holder bars with the line toward the lens. The lens is stopped down to the correct stop for the highlight exposure. A focusing microscope (approximately 40 power) is placed against the glass plate and focused on the line. The screen is then brought as close to the glass as possible, and gradually moved away. When the screen dots that are seen through the microscope barely join up at the corners with a thin connecting line, the screen is in focus.

TURATI FINDER STOP. To focus the screen visually, a special device called a finder stop was suggested by Count V. Turati[1]. This is like a Waterhouse stop except that it has four small holes in it in the form of a square. It is made as follows:

1. Determine the diameter of the principal stop that will be used for the halftone exposure.

2. Use this diameter as a *radius* and draw a circle on the metal blank that will become the stop.

3. Locate four points on the circumference of this circle that are equally distant from one another.

4. At these points drill small holes through the blank. The diameter of the holes should be about 1/100 of the camera

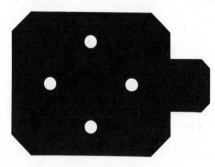

Figure 33   The Finder Stop

extension when it is set at same-size. The stop is now ready for use as follows:

1. Put a piece of line copy on the copyboard. Focus the camera to same-size.

2. Replace the copy with a sheet of white paper.

3. Put the finder stop in the lens barrel and turn on the arcs again.

4. Move the screen forward or backward as far as it will go.

5. Using a magnifier on the ground glass, check the four spots of light that will be seen while the screen is slowly moved into position.

6. When the images of the four spots blend into a single spot, the screen is in focus.

If a multiple-stop exposure system is preferred over the single-stop system, use a stop that is one size larger than the principal stop for the highlight exposure and one size smaller for the detail exposure.

---

(1) L. P. Clerc, *Ilford Manual of Process Work,* Ilford, London, 1941, page 175.

HISLOP'S METHOD OF VISUAL FOCUSING. Another visual method of focusing the screen was suggested by Hislop[1]. In this method, a stop having an opening of one-tenth of an inch or less is used. A microscope is aligned on the optical axis and focused on the underside of the ground glass. Using the flash lamp as a light source, the screen is moved forward and back. As the screen moves, four bright lines due to the diffraction maxima[2] are seen parallel to the sides of the screen aperture. As the screen is moved, the four lines will become two lines and cross at right angles. The point at which the lines cross will be four times as bright as the individual lines. When this point is reached. the screen is in focus.

36C. Screen Setting by Camera Test Exposure. An alternate method of setting the screen was also suggested by Hislop[1]. In this method, a test exposure is made to determine the best halftone dot and, for this, the correct screen distance. The exposure is made through a finder stop having an aperture of one-tenth of an inch or less. When the screen is placed in position, a photographic plate with a commercial type emulsion (not a lith type) is placed in the plate-holding bars at approximately the estimated correct distance. A one-eighth inch spacer of some type is placed on the bottom plate-holding bar so that the plate is angled from the flat screen surface and is one-eighth inch farther from the screen surface at the bottom than at the top. An exposure is made with the flash lamp shooting into the lens for approximately twenty seconds. The image is developed, dried, and examined under the magnifier for the best dot. The screen distance at this point is calculated and used for future settings.

*   *   *

In both of the examples of methods suggested by Hislop, it must be remembered that small apertures are suggested. This is because Hislop is of the opinion that at small apertures diffraction effects predominate, while at large apertures they are secondary to the penumbral effects.

(1) W. B. Hislop, "Some Notes on Diffraction in Halftone Negatives," *Proceedings of the Royal Photographic Society Centenary Conference,* London, 1953, page 517.

(2) Light is often said to travel in straight lines, but it actually bends slightly around the edges of an obstruction. Diffraction is the spreading of this beam of light into the area behind the obstruction. Parallel beams of light passing through the openings of the halftone screen (whose edges act as the obstruction mentioned above) produce a bright spot of light with a few spots of much weaker intensity alongside them. These bright spots are known as the diffraction maxima.

37. EXPOSURE

Of prime importance to a photographer is proper exposure. But, to the halftone photographer proper exposure is something more than just the amount of light required to produce a latent image on a piece of photo-sensitive film. The mechanical ability of the halftone screen to aid in the production of halftone dots is of no value unless the proper exposure through the screen is given to create good dot structure.

The use of such things as multiple stops, light integrators, and flash techniques aid in the creation of a dot that will stand up when exposed onto a metal plate or to repeated dot-etching. Let us look into some of the problems which the photographer must solve to attain proper exposure for halftone dots.

37A. Single- and Multiple-Exposure Systems. As part of usual halftone work with the glass screen, the question arises as to what aperture — or apertures — to use for the exposure.

It is necessary that the photographer accurately reproduce the tonal gradations of the original as a halftone. However, if a distortion of the original tonal values is desired, the photographer must be able to control the type and the amount of the distortion. The problem once again comes back to the question of which stop or combination of stops should be used to obtain the desired result.

To see what a particular aperture does to the reproduction of tone values, let us photograph a gray scale with three different apertures. The ones we will use are f64, f32, and f16, with equivalent exposures.

Figure 34   Effect of Aperture on Tone Reproduction

Without a clear understanding of halftone screen theory, we could assume that a single-stop exposure would allow us to accurately reproduce the gray scale using a halftone screen. You will notice in Figure 34 that this is not the case. The exposure made with the smallest aperture (f64) has recorded the small dots that are required in the shadow area of the negative, but there is not a sufficiently large dot in the highlights to give a good white area on the resultant press print. The exposure made with the medium aperture (f32) has given us fairly good middletone dots, but both the highlight and shadow areas of the print are lacking. With the largest opening (f16) a dot heavy enough to record the highlights is created, but the small dot necessary in the shadow area of the negative is lost on the press print.

From this simple inspection of the results achieved with various apertures, it seems logical that we might be better able to reproduce the entire tonal scale with partial exposures through a combination of two or more apertures. This is how the multiple-stop method of exposure was developed. The photographer noticing the result that was obtained with a single-stop exposure decided to take advantage of what seemed to be the benefits of using multiple stops to cover the tonal range more accurately.

37A-1. THREE-STOP EXPOSURE SYSTEMS. Let us now turn to the other extreme, from the one-stop exposure, and go into some detail on the three-stop method to study its variations.

Where three stops are chosen to record the tones of the original copy, each of these stops has received a name in trade practice. These names are descriptive of the function that each one plays in the reproduction of the tones of the original copy.

The first of the three stops is called the *detail stop*. This is the aperture that is used primarily to record the shadow detail in the negative. It is the smallest of the three apertures that are used and, at same-size reproduction, is usually f45. (NOTE: The significance of the statement "at same-size reproduction," which will be encountered frequently in the balance of this section, is discussed in detail in Section 39.)

The *middletone stop* is the name of the aperture that records mainly the middletone values. At same-size reproduction, it is usually f32.

Finally, to record highlight details we ordinarily use an aperture of f22 at same-size. This aperture is known as the *highlight stop*.

In addition to the apertures listed above, there is a fourth aperture known as the *flash stop*. Although this aperture can be used with the other three stops mentioned, it is not considered as an additional stop when working with a single- or multiple-stop system. Rather, it is an adjunct to the other stops. The function of the flash stop is to put a small overall dot in the halftone. This dot is produced by an exposure through the lens, but with either a piece of white paper over the copy, or with a special lamp set in front of the lens. The copy is *not* used to produce the flash dot. In effect, the flash exposure produces a small, *hard core of silver density* in the center of each and every dot. In this way, a small dot can be built up in the deep shadow areas giving a little additional separation to the deep shadow tones. Although Waterhouse stops are supplied with many lenses to be used as flash apertures, a common procedure is to use an aperture that is two stops smaller than the detail stop. In an ordinary same-size reproduction, this would be an aperture of f90.

RATIO OF THREE-STOP EXPOSURES. When shooting with a three-stop system, the photographer ordinarily will use a ratio of exposures between the detail, middletone, and highlight stops. The 4:2:1 ratio is probably the most common one. This means that the exposure through the detail stop will be four times that of the highlight stop, and the middletone exposure will be twice that of the highlight exposure. When such ratios are discussed, the first number refers to the detail exposure, the second number to the middletone exposure, and the third number refers to the highlight exposure. An example of this ratio might be:

Stop	Exposure	Ratio
Detail	200 seconds	4
Middletone	100 seconds	2
Highlight	50 seconds	1

This 4:2:1 ratio is one that is used with normal copy. Under most conditions it will produce satisfactory results. However, when the copy is not normal, the ratio changes. For example, if the copy has very dense shadows, the detail exposure would have to be increased to record them. Under such conditions the ratio might go as high as 20:4:1. With very flat copy, the highlight exposure must be increased in relation to the other two exposures. When this is the case, the ratio could change to 1:1:8. As copy varies from normal contrast and tonal range toward extreme contrast or extreme

flatness, the ratio of the exposure changes. A greater percentage is given to the detail exposure or the highlight exposure, and considerably less exposure is given to the other stops. Therefore, when the contrast gets very high, the highlight exposure becomes so short that for practical purposes you would be better off without it. This, then, is the reason for the development of the two-stop exposure system — the two stops will cover the necessary tonal range in order to produce a good negative.

37A-2. THE TWO-STOP SYSTEM. Advocates of the two-stop exposure system maintain that two stops will give all the latitude necessary to cover the range of tones that are available in the copy received in the shop. There are two schools of thought as to what apertures to use with the two-stop system. One group maintains that the main portion of the exposure should be the middletone exposure with an additional highlight or detail exposure to bring up the tones of the negative that would otherwise be lacking. The second group believes that the total exposure is made up of highlight and detail exposures, and that the middletones take care of themselves. This occurs, they say, because the two exposures overlap in the middletone areas, and a separate middletone exposure is not necessary.

RATIO OF TWO-STOP EXPOSURES. When the exposures consist of a middletone and either a highlight or detail exposure, the common ratios used are as follows:

    Using detail and middletone exposures:
        Detail Exposure........................ 4
        Middletone exposure..................... 3
    Using middletone and highlight exposures:
        Middletone exposure..................... 6
        Highlight exposure 1

When using detail and highlight exposures without a middletone exposure, the ratios of exposures for contrasty copy are approximately as follows:

        Detail exposure 8
        Highlight exposure 1

For flat copy, these ratios can change to approximately:

        Detail exposure 1
        Highlight exposure 1

The last two ratios will show you how much variation can exist depending upon the characteristics of the copy to be shot. Naturally, when using a method of single- or multiple-stop exposures, it will be necessary for you to experiment with your own equipment and working procedures. Remember that the ratios listed are only to be used as a guide even if they do happen to be used regularly in other plants. They are intended to help you eliminate some of the trial and error that would otherwise occur if you started experimenting on such a procedure without any previous reference.

37A-3. THE SINGLE-STOP SYSTEM. There are increasing numbers of photographers who believe that almost all of the copy that comes into a litho shop can be shot effectively with a single stop. They feel, in general, that the single-stop exposure covers the majority of the tonal range of the subject matter. When the flash is added to this exposure, it fills in the remaining dots needed in the shadow areas of the negative. Thus the single-stop exposure with the flash exposure as a supplement produces the necessary quality in the halftone negative. Certainly it is simpler and less complex to manipulate than multiple-stop exposures.

When the single stop is used, the photographer is guided by the nature of the copy in determining the choice of the particular aperture that he will use. With normal copy, the aperture is usually somewhere between f32 and f22, approximately f27. The exact aperture chosen depends on the screen distance. When flat copy is to be shot, the aperture is set approximately between f22 and f16, or about f19. When the copy is contrasty, the stop that seems to be most used is approximately f39.

38. SOME OBSERVATIONS ON VARIOUS STOP SYSTEMS

All three of the methods described have proponents who will swear that their methods are the best for good-quality reproduction. So it is difficult to give an unbiased answer to the question, "Which exposure system is best?"

The answer perhaps is that no one method is best. Each one offers its own advantages to different individual photographers and probably depends on the way they were trained and the way they think about and visualize the needs of different jobs. The competent halftone photographer should familiarize himself with all three methods, then allow the copy and the situation to help him determine the actual method that should be used for a certain shot.

The one-stop system offers an excellent starting point for the halftone photographer who desires to improve his technical control. It is especially advantageous to the beginning halftone photographer. As he becomes more proficient, he should make experiments with exposures at various apertures and screen distances. Under his own operating conditions he will then see approximately what each aperture will and will not do. He will be able to see what kind of a dot is formed and how much of the tonal scale is covered when a particular aperture is used. Once an understanding is obtained of the approximate range covered with a particular aperture, the photographer has an excellent starting point from which to proceed on his evaluation of whether a one-, two-, or three-stop method of exposure best suits his purpose.

Here is one testing method that will give you a fairly good idea of what a particular aperture will do, and what its importance is in a multiple-stop exposure system:

1. Put a gray scale in your copyboard that has a fairly wide tone range, going from a good, bright white to a deep black. In terms of density readings, this would be a gray scale that ran from a 0.00 density on the white to a 2.00 density in the darkest step. The usual Eastman Kodak paper gray scale will approximate this range.

2. Focus the copy to same-size, and set your lights at the position where you ordinarily like to use them. This is usually at 45 degrees and from 36 to 60 inches away from the copy. Use a separate piece of film for the following five test shots, and process all of them identically.

3. Make an exposure with an f64 aperture in order to obtain the barest pinpoint dot in the shadow area of the negative. You may have to make a few shots at various exposures until you obtain a good one.

4. Make another series of exposures with an f45 aperture to get a pinpoint in the shadow area just as with the f64 exposure.

5. Using the f32 aperture, make exposures to obtain one with a good 50 percent dot in the middle area of the gray scale. If the gray scale has a high density of 0.00, and a low density of 2.00, then a 50 percent dot would be at about the step where the density is 1.00. With a Kodak paper gray scale of 10 steps, the middletone value would be somewhere between Steps 5 and 6. Usually, scales on a reflection densi-

tometer show the midpoint of the scale as being a little closer to the fifth step.

6. Make an exposure with an f22 aperture to get a highlight area that has the smallest possible printing dot.

7. With an f16 aperture, expose for the smallest possible printing dot in the highlight area as you did with the f22 aperture.

When all these negatives are dry, place them on the light table and evaluate them in the following manner:

1. The exposures made with the f64 and f45 apertures can be considered as detail exposures. Therefore, they should record the detail in the shadow areas, and some of the detail in the middletone range. Although they will record in the highlight areas, they will not have created a sufficiently large dot to close up this area. Therefore, compare them to the quality of the shadow dot, and also notice the size of the dot produced in the step that should have a 50 percent tone.

2. The f32 aperture is basically a middletone stop and should produce a good 50 percent value in the middle of the scale. Notice, also, how far up and down the scale it produced acceptable dots both in quality and in proper size.

3. The highlight area is recorded by the f22 and f16 stops which are basically highlight stops. Look at these negatives to see how far down the scale they produced a good dot, and how correct the values are in the steps reproduced.

A test of this sort will enable you to evaluate the negatives and see what the aperture does to both the dot size and the tonal reproduction of the gray scale. In addition, it is an excellent starting point for a further evaluation of the one-, two-, or three-stop systems which can continue along the same lines.

39. MISCELLANEOUS EXPOSURE INFORMATION

This section includes material regarding exposures that cannot be properly classified within the sections of this book, yet should not be left out. They are presented here for your study.

39A. Exposure Changes for Different Magnifications. The majority of work that the average photographer does is at samesize. When a reduction or enlargement is to be made, the amount of light striking the emulsion varies. The exposure or lens aperture must be changed to compensate for the

change in distance between the lens, copyboard, and vacuum back. Many of the commercially available aperture systems provide a means of changing the aperture in proportion to same-size reproduction, holding the exposure constant for any size magnification. The following formula, however, is based on a change in relative exposure for different magnifications with the exposure at same-size being the constant:

$$\text{Relative Exposure} = \frac{(1 + M)^2}{4} \times \text{Exposure at Same-Size}$$

where M = Magnification

To clarify this, let us take the following example for a camera with a diaphragm scale system:

A glossy photograph is to be made into three contact screen halftone negatives. One is to be 100 percent (same-size), a second is to be 200 percent (a two-time enlargement), and the third is to be 30 percent (a reduction to thirty percent of the size of the original). By trial and error, the data of the same-size image showed that it required an exposure of 180 seconds at f32. What is the exposure for the other two sizes?

For the enlargement:

M = 2.00

$$\text{R.E.} = \frac{(1 + 2)^2}{4} \times 180$$

$$\text{R.E.} = \frac{(3)^2}{4} \times 180$$

$$\text{R.E.} = \frac{9}{4} \times 180$$

R.E. = 405 seconds at f32

For the reduction:

M = .30

$$\text{R.E.} = \frac{(1 + .3)^2}{4} \times 180$$

$$\text{R.E.} = \frac{(1.3)^2}{4} \times 180$$

$$\text{R.E.} = \frac{1.69}{4} \times 180$$

R.E. = 76 seconds at f32 (approximately)

39B. Angular Variation of Light Intensity. A photographic lens will not transmit light equally from all portions of the image even if the image had the same reflectivity over its entire area. Let us say, for example, that the light reflected from the copy and passing through the lens along the optical axis had a 100 percent transmission. This is not actually the case, as the lens elements absorb and internally reflect a certain portion of the light. Yet, for the sake of simplifying the following comparison, we will use this figure.

Now, as the light from the copy enters the lens at an angle from the optical axis, a certain portion of the light is lost, thereby reducing the exposure that the area receives. Relative light intensity as the angle from the optical axis is varied, falls off as follows:

Angle From Optical Axis	Relative Light Intensity
0°	100.0%
5°	98.4%
10°	94.1%
15°	87.0%
20°	78.0%
25°	67.5%
40°	34.4%
60°	6.2%

These are numerical values expressed by the "cosine fourth" law which is written as "$\cos^4 \phi$."[1] This law says that illumination through a lens will be reduced to $E \cos^4 \phi$ as the angle ϕ varies from the optical axis. In this formula, "E" is equal to the illumination on the axis of the lens.

---

(1) In a right-angle triangle, the cosine (cos) of an angle is obtained by dividing the length of the side adjacent to the angle by the length of the hypotenuse of the triangle. In the following diagram, the cosine of the angle $Q = \frac{B}{C}$.

In LTF's text, *Offset Stripping, Black-and-White,* Chapter 2 includes an excellent explanation of the use of this mathematical tool by the lithographer.

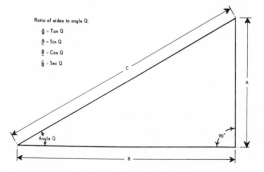

Ratio of sides to angle Q:

$\frac{A}{B}$ = Tan Q

$\frac{A}{C}$ = Sin Q

$\frac{B}{C}$ = Cos Q

$\frac{C}{B}$ = Sec Q

39C. The Use of the f64 Stop. Although the f45 aperture is considered the normal detail stop in a three-stop system when exposure is made through a glass halftone screen, some photographers advocate the use of the f64 aperture for this purpose. Occasionally pinpoint dots are necessary and supply important detail to the picture area. A flash dot cannot be used because of the expanse of area where no dot is required. Then, the additional time required for an exposure made through the f64 aperture is well worthwhile. The f64 exposure will produce dots that have a smooth tone rather than the jumpy character that is occasionally produced by the f45 aperture where the individual dot develops with a ragged shape rather than as a true circle.

Table V
HALFTONE FAILURES

In evaluating a halftone negative the photographer considers, first, the general contrast of the entire negative. He considers, second, the quality of the negative. Freedom from spots, streaks, and stains, and uniform density is also desirable.

The following tabulation indicates the most common causes of defective halftone negatives with suggested remedies:

DEFECTS	CAUSES	REMEDIES
1. Incorrect contrast. The opaque dots in the denser areas (highlights) overlap (no clear dots remain) and the opaque dots in the light areas (shadows) are too small. Negatives of this type produce plates in which the small dots are missing in the highlights while the shadows are solid and lack detail. Also fogged highlight dots and shadow dots that are too small or too weak.	(a) Screen is too far from the sensitive material.	(a) Check the screen distance with calibrated wedge.
	(b) Overexposure with the highlight stop.	(b) Decrease the highlight exposure.
	(c) Highlight stop is too large.	(c) Use a highlight stop which bears a closer relation to that specified by the screen equation.
	(d) Failure to use a flash exposure.	(d) Using a small diaphragm aperture, flash the negative by placing a piece of enamel or coated white paper over the copy.
	(e) Tonal range of the copy is too great.	(e) Make an additional exposure with a small stop or increase the detail exposure which may have been insufficient.
2. Incorrect contrast. Either the opaque dots in the denser areas (highlights) are too small (the clear dots are too large), or the opaque dots in the light areas (shadows) are too large, or both. A negative of this type is termed "flat."	(a) The stop used for the highlight exposure is too small.	(a) For average halftone made with two stops and a flash, the highlight stop should bear the relationship of 1:44 to the camera extension. With weak lights or slow sensitive materials, it is impossible to use a stop whose relation is 1:38 or 1:32 to the camera extension.
	(b) The screen distance is too short.	(b) Examine the screen setting and distance.
	(c) Insufficient highlight exposure.	(c) Highlights which are too open because of insufficient exposure

DEFECTS	CAUSES	REMEDIES
		must be judged more carefully. If one stop and a flash exposure were used, it is possible that the stop was too small. If a highlight and detail and a flash exposure are given, the highlight exposure may require additional time. With the three-stop method the middle-tone exposure affects the highlight dots to some extent, so a slight increase of the middle-tone exposure may be all that is necessary to decrease the size of the highlight dots. An increase of the highlight exposure will, however, be more effective.
	(d) The detail and flash exposure are too long.	(d) Decrease the detail and flash exposure duration.
	(e) The flash stop was too large.	(e) Make the flash exposure with a small round diaphragm aperture whose relations to camera extension is between 1/128 and 1/256.
3. Incorrect dot formation. Dots have soft edges. Such dots will not produce satisfactory press plates as light readily penetrates them. Fuzzy dots are also incapable of holding light back and thus form larger printing dots on the press plate.	(a) Screen distance too long.	(a) Obtain correct screen distance for the screen in use.
	(b) Incorrect stop or stops.	(b) Stops should be of a size proportional to the camera extension.
	(c) Halftone screen and sensitive material are not parallel.	(c) Check the parellelism of the planes of the screen and sensitive material.
	(d) Underdeveloped negative due to insufficient developing time or worn out or oxidized developing solution.	(d) Develop according to the manufacturer's instructions. Use fresh developer. Pour out and dilute enough developing solution to fill the tray 1 or 2 inches deep just before use. For single halftone negatives, use fresh developing solution for each negative. When developing batches of negatives at one time, use fresh developer for each six to ten negatives. The rate of deterioration of the developer depends upon its use and its exposure to the air. The discoloration of the developer indicates the degree of oxidation.
	(e) Temperature of developing solution is too low.	(e) Developer temperature should be 65° – 70°F. or 18° – 21°C.
4. Incorrect dot formation: square shadow dots and square transparent highlight dots.	(a) Screen distance is too short.	(a) Recheck the screen distance. Obtain correct screen distance for the screen in use.
	(b) Stops are too small.	(b) Use a larger set of stops.
	(c) Flash stop too large and exposure too long.	(c) Use a smaller stop for flashing. Shorten the flash exposure.
5. Transparent dots are fogged.	(a) Exposure to extraneous light.	(a) Use the proper safe-lights for the sensitive material in use. Use sensitive materials prior to the date of expiration. See that the container of the sensitive materials does not leak. Close all cracks through which light can enter the darkroom.
	(b) Lack of bromide in the developer.	(b) Compound the developing solution strictly according to formula.
6. Double dots and Moiré.	(a) Camera vibration during the exposure.	(a) Check camera for contact with the wall of the darkroom. Avoid moving the camera or its parts during the exposure. The concussion of air caused by slamming a darkroom door will cause vibration and, therefore, should be avoided.

DEFECTS	CAUSES	REMEDIES
	(b) Stops are not concentric.	(b) See that iris diaphragm functions properly.
	(c) Loose stayflat or vacuum back.	(c) See that the stayflat and vacuum back are stationary.
	(d) Halation, or light, reflected from the back of the sensitive material.	(d) Use antihalation sensitive materials. Cover shiny spots on the vacuum back with dull black paint; also the camera back.
	(e) Patterns in the copy.	(e) The moiré pattern can be diminished and often removed by changing the angle of the screen or changing the position of the copy, if the screen cannot be rotated.
7. Variation in dot size and shape from one side of the negative to the other.	(a) Improper alignment of the screen with the vacuum back or stayflat which holds the sensitive plate.	(a) Check parallelism of the planes of the screen and the sensitive material with a graduated wedge. Check the position of the plateholder bridge of the camera.
	(b) Uneven illumination.	(b) Check the position of the arc lamps and the evenness of the illumination.
8. Weak, soft dots in the shadows with open highlights.	(a) Underdevelopment.	(a) Develop the negative for the recommended time at the proper temperature.
	(b) Underexposure.	(b) Expose the negative with the proper stop, or stops, for the necessary time to produce a satisfactory dense negative.
9. Weak, soft dots in the shadows with correct highlight dots.	(a) Improper screen distance.	(a) Correct the screen distance.
	(b) Failure to flash the negative.	(b) Flash for the required time to produce satisfactory shadow dots.
10. Spots, streaks, and blotches.	(a) Dirt on the screen or on the sensitive material.	(a) Clean the green with lens' cleaning tissue or a soft chamois. Occasional use of lens or screen cleaning fluid will help remove grease or spots. Remove dust by snapping the back of the film or by brushing with a clean camel's hair brush.
	(b) Uneven immersion in the developing solution.	(b) Developer streaks can be eliminated by more even immersion of the negative in the developing solution.
	(c) Too little developer in the tray.	(c) Increase so more even development can be accomplished.
	(d) Insufficient agitation during development, especially during the early stages.	(d) Agitation improves the uniformity of the halftone negative.
	(e) Failure to place the sensitive material flatly on the vacuum back or stayflat.	(e) Lay the sensitive material flat on the vacuum back or brush it flat on the stayflat.
11. Brown negatives.	(a) Worn-out or oxidized developer.	(a) Use fresh developer for all halftones.
	(b) High temperature of the developing solution.	(b) Develop at $65°-70°$F. or $18°-21°$C.
	(c) Under development in an attempt to compensate for overexposure.	(c) Expose negative correctly.
12. Green brown negative.	(a) Overdevelopment in an attempt to compensate for under exposure. (This does not happen with all developers.)	(a) The time required for development should not exceed 20 to 30 seconds for film when all other conditions are standard. Develop for the recommended time.

Chapter X

PRINCIPLES OF THE CONTACT SCREEN

The last fifteen years have seen a revolution in halftone photography. The contact screen has been a very important factor in this tremendous change in the method of producing halftone images. Although not a new idea, it is only during the last few years that the contact screen has been widely used in lithographic plants.

40. DEVELOPMENT OF THE CONTACT SCREEN

Instead of the opaque crosslines and transparent squares that make up the conventional glass screen, the contact screen has a pattern of small dot areas on it. The dots are vignetted — that is, they gradually decrease in density from their centers to their edges. In use, the screen is held in contact with the sensitive emulsion while an exposure is made through it.

Ever since this method was first suggested by Berchtold[1] in 1855, there have been numerous attempts to produce a satisfactory contact screen. The original screen had dots of metallic silver which had a tendency to scatter the light passing through them. This was one of the objections that made the contact screen impractical in the early days of its development. However, when the silver image was replaced by a dye image, this major objection disappeared.

The objections to the early silver contact screen were compared to the early objections to the glass screen in a paper delivered in 1942[2]. They were as follows:

(1) A. J. Berchtold, British Patent Number 426, 1855.
(2) J. A. C. Yule, F. B. Johnson, A. Murray, "A New Type of Contact Halftone Screen," *J. Franklin Institute,* Volume 234, Number 6, December 1942.

"The main disadvantages of the crossline screen are:

1. High cost of screen and mechanism for operation.

2. Skill and training required to obtain good results.

3. Imperfect tone reproduction in the finished halftone requiring hand correction, especially in the highlights.

4. Loss of sharpness of detail due to diffraction with the finer screen rulings.

"On the other hand, the contact screen, as it had been known up to now, had an even more formidable array of objections. These included:

1. Too little control of contrast.

2. Extreme sensitivity to the presence of dust specks between screen and film.

3. Poor tone reproduction.

4. No improvement in sharpness over the crossline screen, in spite of the elimination of diffraction effects.

5. Short life of screens due to ease of scratching.

6. Formation of Newton's rings in the layers of air between the screen and the film."

When the silver image of the contact screen was replaced with a dye image, the same authorities[1], quoted previously, reported:

"In experimenting with clear dye contact screens, it generally became evident that the dye image opened the way to a sweeping elimination of all the supposed deficiencies of vignetted dot screens. Eventually, the following advances over the prior art in contact screen process could be claimed:

1. Almost no dispersion of light by screen or continuous-tone negative.

2. Wide range of contrast control with a single screen.

3. No out-of-contact effect around dust specks.

4. No Newton rings.

5. Fully corrected tone reproduction built into screen.

6. Halftone dot quality is independent of contrast of copy."

For a moment, let us overlook these claims and try to see just what advantages the contact screen offers to the halftone photographer of today. They can best be summed up as two factors — speed and ease of operation.

Making halftones with a contact screen is considerably faster (about five times) than with a glass screen. In a recent

---

(1) J. A. C. Yule, F. B. Johnson, A. Murray, "Better Halftones," *The National Lithographer,* November 1941.

test made with the same copy and identical camera set-up, and using the two screens, the contact screen took a total of 43 seconds, while the exposure through the glass screen took 225 seconds.

The screen is also simple to handle. Although you have to put it up on the vacuum back with every piece of film being shot, the halftone is shot through a single stop. This results in a considerable saving of time compared with multiple-stop exposure systems used with glass screens. In addition, the contact screen offers an improvement in sharpness and better image resolution. This improves the reproduction of fine detail. Variations of contrast are simpler to obtain with the contact screen than with the glass crossline screen; there is no need for the careful setting of screen distance. You only have to assure good contact to obtain a good dot structure.

41. THE ORANGE CONTACT SCREEN

The orange contact screen was the first contact screen marketed by Eastman Kodak. This screen was designed for making positives. It is practically non-existent today. However, for the purpose of historical information, the following brief discussion of its use is included.

A continuous-tone negative of the copy was shot to the required size and developed in a magenta dye-coupling developer. This produced a dyed-image continuous-tone negative. This negative was placed over the orange contact screen and an orthochromatic film was placed under the screen in a vacuum frame. Partial exposures were made to a special lamp through yellow and magenta filters. The product was a halftone positive ready for deep-etch platemaking. In the event a negative was desired, it was contacted from the halftone positive.

42. THE MAGENTA CONTACT SCREEN

To combat some of the early difficulties with the orange contact screen, the Magenta Contact Screen was introduced by Eastman Kodak. This screen produced a halftone negative directly, did not require as much processing time, and did not require special developer such as one containing paraphenylenediamine derivatives which can cause skin troubles or dermatitis. In addition, a special printing lamp was not required and there was no need for the intermediate continuous-tone negative.

The first methods of using the Magenta Contact Screen also called for filters to control the contrast of halftone negatives. A magenta filter (Wratten No. 30) increased the halftone negative contrast, and a yellow filter (Wratten No. 4) decreased contrast.

MAGENTA FILTERED   YELLOW FILTERED

Figure 35   Contrast Control by Use of Colored Filters With the Magenta Contact Screen

In process color work, the magenta and yellow Kodak CC filters of various densities offer a convenient means to control the contrast of halftone positives made from continuous tone separation negatives.

In shooting halftone negatives, the photographer will find that he rarely has to use the magenta filter except when reproducing an extremely flat original. For the average job that comes into the plant, the white light exposure will provide sufficient contrast. With the original method of using filters to control the contrast of the negative, a flash exposure was recommended only when shooting extremely high contrast originals.

In addition to these factors, a quick transition to the Magenta Contact Screen was delayed because few cameras had a vacuum film holder. The screen had growing pains; many expected it to cure all glass screen troubles. Dot density varied in the early screens; better developers, films, and a more satisfactory system had to be found.

Eventually, Eastman Kodak presented two new methods of handling the Magenta Contact Screen to produce improved halftones. These methods use no filters, are faster, and have replaced the filter method almost completely. They are called the controlled-flash method and the highlighting method.

In addition, it was found that a very wide range of contrast control is possible simply by varying development procedures or reversing the position of the screen emulsion. For example, the exposed film can be developed with agitation until the image starts to appear and then left in the tray to still-develop for an additional time. This gives a longer scale of tones than with full agitation. In addition, the screen can be turned over and the film exposed through the back. This produces a negative having high contrast.

LIMITATION OF THE MAGENTA CONTACT SCREEN. Because the Magenta Contact Screen has a colored dye image, it leads to one difficulty which should be mentioned here. It cannot be used to photograph colored originals directly due to the light-filtering action of the dye color. In most cases this is no great problem as the halftone photographer does not often work with colored originals. However, the Magenta Contact Screen can be used to make halftones from colored originals when an indirect process is used (see Chapter XVI, Section 65).

43. THE GRAY (NEUTRAL) CONTACT SCREEN

Neutral tone screens have very definite advantages when used for process color work. They can also be used for black-and-white halftone work, especially when the originals have color in them. The advantage of this type of screen is that it does not affect the color in an original as is the case with the Magenta Contact Screen. Using the magenta screen, the contrast will change depending upon the color that is being photographed. Basically you are getting the effect of a filter being used through the screen. With the gray screens, however, this is not the case.

The methods of handling the gray screen are basically similar to the methods of handling the Magenta Contact Screen. Briefly, the typical halftone is exposed by a main exposure and a flash exposure. There is no need for filters to control contrast. Various techniques to increase contrast with colored screens, such as shooting through the back of the screen, or using acetate sheeting between the emulsion of the film and the screen can also be used just as readily with the gray screen.

One of the original problems that existed with gray contact screens was that they showed the effect of high vacuum much more readily than the magenta screen. This was because they did not contain an optically clear dye. The problems arose due to the collection of dust between the screen and the film. And, in the older days, when high pressure in vacuum frames or on camera backs was the vogue, these effects with the gray contact screen created difficult problems. However, within the last few years the effects of high pressure have been noted. Indications are that it is better to use minimum rather than maximum pressures. Once this general approach became effective, the gray contact screen no longer had its earlier disadvantages. At the present time it is quite capable of producing completely satisfactory halftones.

Although most rectangular screens, either glass or contact, are made with the angle of the screen at 45° it is possible to get gray contact screens with angles other than 45°. This allows the use of gray contact screens for direct color separations at the correct angles with no need to buy a more expensive larger screen and cutting a section out of it.

Chapter XI

MAKING HALFTONES WITH THE CONTACT SCREEN

The contact screen as it exists today is not the final answer for all reproduction requirements. The characteristics of the printing process determine the desired characteristics of the halftone negative that must be produced for it. Therefore, the dots that make up the screen image must be designed for the best possible tone reproduction with a given process and for a given quality of reproduction.

In designing the Magenta Contact Screen, Eastman Kodak considered the most probable applications of the screen. In effect, they made a screen that will be useful to photographers under a wide variety of conditions. However, it seems reasonable to believe that even better screens will be made in the not too distant future. To quote from the writings of Paul W. Dorst on this matter:

". . . it should be possible to make contact screens for offset lithography, for photoengraving, or for invert halftone processes, with distortions built into the screen to compensate for tone changes in the process itself. Thus it should be possible to eliminate, or greatly reduce, hand retouching for black-and-white reproductions in many instances. It is even possible that tone distortions might be built into special screens for color separation, and thus reduce the work of color correction. Obviously this could not be done in all cases, on the basis of our present information, but for certain types of work it appears to be possible."[1]

(1) Paul W. Dorst, "A Method of Designing and Making Contact Screens," *Research Bulletin* #216, Lithographic Technical Foundation, Inc., New York, 1951, page 88.

Some of these ideas have partly come into existence in the newest contact screens. We now have two basic types of screens: (1) a positive type for shooting halftone positives from continuous tone negatives and (2) a negative type for shooting halftone negatives from continuous tone positives. In addition, some contact screens have elliptical or chain shaped dots. At the approximate 50 per cent dot area, the dots join in one direction before they join in another direction. This softens the sudden density increase in the tone reproduction curve of conventional screens at the approximate 50 per cent dot areas.

44. CONTRAST AND TONE RANGE WITH THE MAGENTA SCREEN

The contact screen is a dynamic tool for the photolithographer. Since its inception, it has changed in many ways and the methods of handling it have varied also. The magenta screens were made that particular color to give the photographer a control over contrast. The use of exposures through a yellow or rose filter allows the photographer to get negatives with high or low contrast; with white light he got a normal contrast. This early method, of using filters for contrast, is still used with positive working magenta contact screens. With negative working screens, however, it has been found that the use of different exposure and developing techniques give even better control over contrast than can be obtained with colored filters. Two of these procedures are the "controlled-flash" method and the "highlighting" method.

44A. The Controlled-Flash Method. This is the first method proposed by Kodak to improve the halftone images made with the Magenta Contact Screen. It is based on a two-step exposure. The basic exposure is made to white light alone. The highlight density of the original copy is the main factor in determining this exposure. Under normal conditions, however, this exposure to white light will not produce a satisfactory dot in the shadow area of the negative. According to Kodak[1], "The shadow exposure is insufficient by an amount which depends upon the density range of the original copy."

To remedy this situation, Kodak proposes to bring up the size of the shadow dot by flash exposure. In this way the

(1) "Improved Halftones With the Kodak Magenta Contact Screens," *Kodak Data Sheet,* Published October 1950, Eastman Kodak Company, Rochester, N. Y.

flash exposure, to some extent, controls the tonal range of the resulting negative. At first glance this seems to be a direct contradiction of the earlier Kodak proposal — that the flash exposure is used only for originals of high contrast. However, this is not the case, for the flash is actually lowering the contrast while extending the lower scale of the tones reproduced.

To use this method, a special flashing lamp must be set up. This lamp is made from a Kodak Adjustable Safelight. A Wratten Series 00 filter is used with a 7 1/2-watt frosted bulb in the lamp. The flashing exposure will average from 15 to 30 seconds when the lamp is kept 6 feet away from the sensitive emulsion. This lamp should be positioned so that it will be centered and will evenly illuminate the vacuum back when it is opened. The procedure to determine the basic flash exposure is as follows:

1. Set up a yellow-light flashing lamp for your process camera in the darkroom. (See figure 36.)

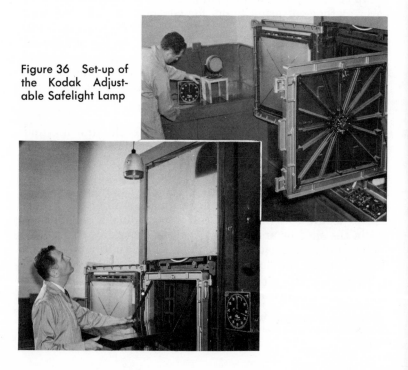

Figure 36   Set-up of the Kodak Adjustable Safelight Lamp

Figure 37   The Kodak Graphic Arts Exposure Computer

2. Cut a strip of lith type ortho film and place it on the camera back. Put the contact screen over the strip of film.

3. Expose the strip to a series of direct exposures to the flashing lamp through the screen. These exposures may be in 5 second increments or in ten second increments depending on the speed of the film.

4. Develop, stop, and fix the film strip according to the recommendations of the film manufacturer.

5. Inspect the film strip to determine which exposure time produced a shadow dot of normal size. This time is referred to as the *basic flash exposure time.* The actual time for the flash exposure used in making a halftone will be a fraction of this basic flash exposure time which you compute.

To compute the exact flash exposure required for a particular piece of copy exposed through a particular screen you must know (1) the basic density range of the screen and (2) the density range of the copy.

The density range of the screen is the range of densities that the screen can reproduce without additional flashing, highlighting, or still development.[1] A screen's range is usually less than

[1]The procedure to determine the basic density range of a contact screen is as follows: (1) Shoot a gray scale through the screen. Give enough exposure to produce highlights that are at least as closed up as normal highlight dots. If the highlights are too open, another negative

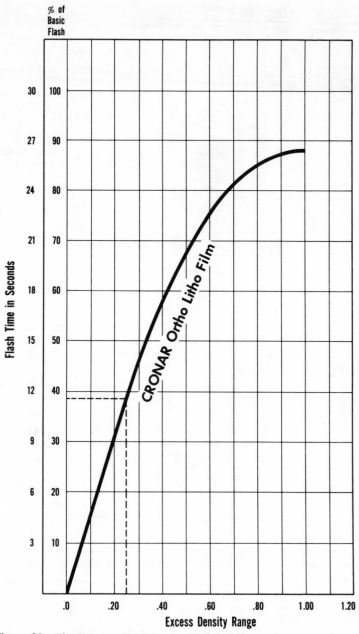

Figure 38   The Du Pont Shadow Flash Computer

the density range of most copy. To determine the density range of the copy, subtract its lowest density from its highest density. Now, subtract the screen range from the copy range. The difference is the excess density of the copy. With this figure you can now compute the exact flash exposure required with a Kodak Graphic Arts Computer or the DuPont Shadow Flash Computer.

The steps to produce a halftone are as follows:

1. Place the copy in the camera copy holder. Focus the camera to produce the image size desired and position the lights.

2. Place a sheet of lith type ortho film on the camera back, emulsion side up. Place the contact screen over the film with its emulsion side down.

3. Give the film its main exposure through the lens.

4. Open the camera back and give the film the yellow-light flash exposure for the time that you previously computed.

5. Develop the film according to the manufacturer's recommendations.

6. Inspect the negative. If the highlight dots are too open, make another negative and increase the main exposure time. If the shadow dots are too small when the main exposure time is correct, increase the flash exposure time.

44B. The Highlighting Method. This is the second method proposed by Eastman Kodak to improve the quality of negatives obtained with the Magenta Contact Screen. The controlled-flash method is still used to control contrast in this process. However, we now add two additional items to the method. These are: 1) Still development, and 2) A highlight exposure made without the contact screen which is called a highlighting exposure. The purpose of using still development is to increase the sharpness of detail. However, still development will lower the contrast of a negative at the same time. So, to compensate for this lowering of contrast, an exposure is made with-

---

should be made with more exposure. Do not flash or highlight the test halftone. (2) Develop the film according to the film manufacturer's recommendations for time, temperature, and agitation. (3) After fixing, inspect the negative with a magnifier. Determine which of the original gray scale steps produced the size of highlight and shadow dots in the negative that are suitable for your work. (4) Determine the densities of these steps on the original gray scale. (5) Subtract the lowest from the highest of these two densities. The remainder is the basic density range of the screen.

out the contact screen. This is basically the combination line and halftone exposure discussed in Chapter 16, Section 61B. Kodak suggests that the time of agitation in the developer be kept constant. Otherwise, there are too many variables in the process for accurate control. The method is as follows:

First, determine the basic flash exposure time. Follow the same steps described on page 114 except for the development procedure. Agitate the developer for a few seconds and then immerse the film. Continue the agitation for 1½ minutes. Then allow the film to remain perfectly still in the developer until development is complete. These times of agitation and still development are suggestions for a start for the test. You may wish later to vary the time of agitation according to the contrast you want.

As before, inspect the film and find out which exposure time produced a shadow dot of normal size. This is the basic flash exposure. The actual flash exposure will be some fraction of this time that you determine with the computer.

The steps in making a highlighted halftone negative are as follows:

1. Place the copy in the camera copy holder. Focus the camera and position the lights.

2. Place a sheet of lith type ortho film on the camera back emulsion side up. Place the contact screen over the film with its emulsion side down.

3. Flash the film with the flashing lamp through the screen for the time you computed.

4. Close the camera back and make the main exposure to the copy through the lens.

5. With the vacuum still on, open the camera back, remove the screen, and reclose the back.

6. Make the highlighting exposure to the copy through the lens. The exposure time can be up to about ten per cent of the main exposure.

7. Develop the film with controlled agitation as was done when the basic flash exposure was determined.

8. Inspect the negative. If the highlight dots are too open, increase *both* the main and highlight exposure times in the same proportion. If the highlight dots are too small, decrease both the main and highlight exposure times in the same proportion. If the shadow dots are too small when the main and highlight exposures are correct, increase the flash exposure.

Negative type contact screens have some "built-in" highlight exposure. With such a screen you will need less highlight exposure or none at all.

The advantages of these methods of using the contact screen are that they increase the quality of the tonal range within the highlight area. One of the previous faults of contact screens was that the highlight areas lacked contrast when most of the rest of the scale was correct. In addition, the flashing method inside the darkroom is more convenient and eliminates the need to go outside to set a lamp in position to flash through the lens.

There seems to be no question that agitation during development has a considerable effect on negatives shot through a contact screen. For this reason, established procedure should be standardized to conditions within a single plant. Haphazard methods of operation will cause variations in the end results.

It is of extreme importance that good contact be maintained between the screen and the film being exposed. If this is not the case, then the areas that have poor contact will become areas of increased contrast on the resulting negative.

A technique that has recently come into use to get greatly added contrast with the contact screen is to turn the screen over and shoot through the back of the screen. In effect this adds distance (the thickness of the screen base) between the screen surface and the sensitive emulsion. This separation greatly increases the contrast of the resultant negative. A similar effect can also be produced by inserting a clear piece of film between the screen surface and sensitive emulsion. The thickness of this film will determine the contrast obtained. This technique is one that must be experimented with before put into use. However, it is a most effective technique with very flat copy.

Variations in line voltage will cause contrast fluctuations in the negative produced. Just as the colored filters are used to change the contrast of the negative, a variation in the line voltage will not only cause changes of light intensity, but variations in the color composition of the light emitted by the source. The effect, then, is the same as that produced when exposing through a filter. It is important, therefore, that the line voltage be kept as constant as possible.

Chapter XII

DENSITOMETRY AND THE DENSITOMETER

At some time or another, we all have received such instructions as "Make it a bit darker," "It's got to be a bit more punchy," "Print it a shade lighter," and other similar statements. The speakers were referring to tones or contrasts of picture areas and describing how they should be changed to make them more suitable. The trouble with the information they were giving is that it could mean different things to different people. How much is "just a shade darker"? Is it 2 percent, 3 percent, 5 percent, or 25 percent? You must remember that our numerical system is a means of accurate measurement as well as a common language. When you ask a person to cut a piece of lumber 36 inches long, you expect to get a piece of the correct size. Both you and the man doing the cutting are measuring with a scale that holds the same meaning for each of you. It is only through measurement that you are able to exercise control. More specific values of tones could have been given in the quotations above if numerical values were used instead of general terms. The study and use of densitometry make it possible to designate tones and contrasts more accurately by measuring them and giving them a numerical value.

45. DENSITOMETRIC TERMS AND DEFINITIONS

Let us begin by explaining what is meant by density. *Density* is the term used to describe the relative tone value of an area. Actually, we use it to tell how much darker or lighter one area is than another. The darker the area, the denser it is. When we refer to an area that allows light to be passed or transmitted through it, we are speaking of *transmission density*. When we refer to an area that reflects light, we are speaking of *reflection density*. In its more technical application, density is a means of measuring and expressing the tone of an area in the form of a number. This number is based on the amount of light that is transmitted through or reflected from an area.

If we allow light to pass through a negative or positive, part of the light will be absorbed by the material, and part will pass through. In passing through, however, a portion of the light is scattered by the small silver particles within the emulsion that make up the image. In density measurements we speak of two types of density — *diffuse* and *specular*. Diffuse density is the density measured at the surface of an image. It measures all the light passing through the image at that point. It is measured by densitometers and is useful for measurements to make contact exposures. Specular density is measured at a distance from the image. It is the effective density for images projected by lenses in process cameras.

Both specular and diffuse densities would be the same if the image did not scatter any light at all. For this reason, diffuse and specular densities more closely approximate each other in dye images such as are in color transparencies rather than the usual negatives or positives that have metallic silver images. This is because dye images scatter less light than the silver-grain images.

A relationship between specular and diffuse densities was established by Callier[1]. He adopted the symbols "$D_\parallel$" to represent specular density and "D_H" to represent diffuse density. The ratio of these two quantities was designated as "Q". Since that time this ratio has been known as the *Q factor* or *Callier factor*. As a mathematical formula, this ratio appears as follows:

$$Q = \frac{D_\parallel}{D_H}$$

In general, the Q factor will vary depending upon the granularity of the film or plate being measured. The higher the grain of the emulsion, the higher the factor. Values from 1.00 for a basically grainless image, to 1.90 for a fast emulsion with considerable grain, can be considered the approximate range of values obtained.

---

(1) A. Callier, *Photographic Journal,* 49, (n.s. 33), 1909, page 200.

When speaking of the light rays that strike an image, we normally refer to three types of rays. The rays coming from the light source and striking the surface of the material are known as *incident rays*. After striking an opaque surface, the rays that are reflected from this surface are known as *reflected rays*. Those incident rays passing through the image are known as the *transmitted rays* after they have emerged from the material. A numerical value can be assigned to the *transmittance* or *reflectance* of a material depending upon how much of the incident light is reflected or transmitted. Thus, a tone area that will transmit one-half of the incident rays that fall upon it would be said to have a transmittance of 50 percent.

In equation form, this is shown as $T = \dfrac{I_t}{I_i}$ where T = the transmission, I_t the intensity of the transmitted light, and I_i the intensity of the incident light.

Another term used in the study of densitometry is *opacity*. Opacity is defined as the ratio of the incident light to the transmitted light, and it is therefore the reciprocal[1] of the transmission previously discussed. In equation form this is shown as follows:

$$O = \frac{I_i}{I_t}$$

Using these terms, density is defined as the logarithm[2] (to the base 10) of the reciprocal of the transmission. This could also be the logarithm (to the base 10) of the opacity. This relationship appears as follows:

$$D = \log_{10} \frac{1}{T} = \log_{10} O$$

Density values can and have been computed with the use of these formulas. However, as density, transmission, and opacity tables are available, there is no necessity for the

---

(1) To get the reciprocal of a number, divide one by the number. For example, the reciprocal of 5 is 1/5.

(2) A logarithm is a number indicating the power to which another number — known as the "base" — is raised to produce a given positive number. For example, 2 is the logarithm of the positive number 100 to the base 10. It is written as follows: $\log_{10} 100 = 2$

Complex calculations can be shortened by the use of logarithms. Multiplication can be simplified to a process of adding logarithms. Division can be simplified to a process of subtracting logarithms.

lithographer to go to the laborious task of computing his own tables (see Appendix).

46. THE RELATIONSHIP BETWEEN DENSITY AND EXPOSURE

With a given development, a relationship exists between the exposure of a sensitive material and the density produced upon it. This relationship can be shown as a curve drawn on a graph. The curve is named after the men who first developed it. The men were Hurter and Driffield, and the curve became known as the *H and D curve*. It is also known as the *D logE curve,* or the *characteristic curve.*

To plot the H and D curve, it is necessary to expose a sensitive material to light in a series of exposure steps that bear a known relationship to each other. For example, each step can be exposed twice the length of time of the previous step. An illustration of this would be steps which were exposed for the following times: 1, 2, 4, 8, 16, 32, ... seconds. When the resulting negative is developed, the densities are read for each step, and the curve is constructed by plotting the densities on the vertical axis, and the exposure times on the horizontal axis. However, due to the large range of exposure

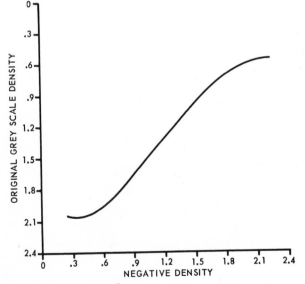

Figure 39   A Characteristic Curve

values that would be obtained, the densities are plotted against the logarithms of the exposures, for the sake of convenience. This brought about the use of the name D logE curve, where the densities are plotted against the logarithm of the exposures.

When photographing a gray scale, we have the equivalent of a stepped series of exposures. The curve then can be constructed by plotting the densities of the original positive gray scale on the vertical axis against the densities of the resulting negative on the horizontal axis. This is shown in Figure 39.

The curve is divided into three broad areas. The first of these is the *toe* of the curve. This area is often referred to as the region of underexposure. The next section of the curve is called the *straight-line portion*. This area is usually considered the region of correct exposure. The third portion of the curve is called the *shoulder*. It is basically the region of overexposure.

The straight-line portion of the curve is the area that most concerns us. Within this area, density and the logarithm of the exposure (D vs. logE) are proportional. In both the shoulder and the toe of the curve there is no constant relationship between density and logE. For this reason it is difficult for the average photographer to make accurate measurements and calculations within these two areas.

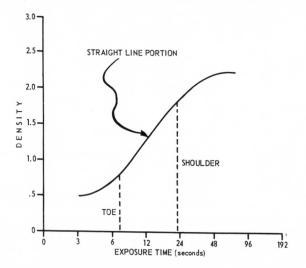

Figure 40　Areas of the Characteristic Curve

One other factor that can be determined from the D logE curve is the contrast that has been produced by a given development. This is obtained from the slope of the curve or the angle that the straight-line portion of the curve makes with the base line. The steeper the slope (the larger the angle), the greater the contrast. The less the slope, the lower the contrast.

It is also known that the contrast will increase with prolonged development and decrease with shortened development. Thus, contrast is dependent upon development, and we use the term *gamma* (symbolized by the Greek letter γ) to designate the contrast obtainable through development. To quote from C. B. Neblette[1]:

"The slope of the straight-line portion of the D logE curve, of the tangent of the angle[2] between it and the logE axis, being indicative of the difference in density, it is therefore also a measure of the degree of development or *gamma*.

"Gamma is thus the ratio of the difference between any two densities on the straight-line portion of the D logE curve and the difference in the logarithms of the corresponding exposures, or $\gamma = \dfrac{D_2 - D_1}{\log E_2 - \log E_1}$."

In this statement, Neblette has pointed out that the slope of the straight-line portion of the characteristic curve indicates the difference in density, and is therefore a measure of gamma. Most of us are also familiar with the statement that a straight line can be defined by two points. By tying these two statements together, we can come up with a practical means for the densitometric measurement of gamma.

Let us take our maximum and minimum densities on the straight-line portion of the characteristic curve to be the two points that define the straight line, or in this case the characteristic curve. By subtracting the minimum value from the

(1) C. B. Neblette, *Photography, Its Principles and Practice,* D. Van Nostrand Company, New York, 4th Edition, 1942, page 412.

(2) In a right-angle triangle, the tangent of an angle is obtained by dividing the length of the side opposite the angle by the length of the side adjacent to the angle. In the following diagram the tangent of the angle $Q = \dfrac{A}{B}$.

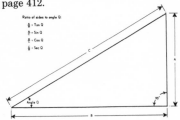

maximum value, we have a single number which we call the
density range. This density range (D.R.) figure shows us the
contrast just as a gamma value would do. The higher the density range, the higher the contrast. The lower the density
range, the lower the contrast.

To tie this in to practical use, let us assume a copy whose
D.R. (measured on a densitometer) is 1.70. When we shoot a
negative of this original, the resulting negative has a density
range of 1.40 measured on the same two points which were
read on the copy. The gamma of this negative, showing the
change in contrast due to development, can be obtained by
substituting the proper values in the following formula:

$$\gamma = \frac{\text{D.R. of negative}}{\text{D.R. of copy}}$$

In this example, the value would be:

$$\gamma = \frac{1.40}{1.70} = .82$$

Up to this point we have been discussing only a single D
logE curve of a particular emulsion. We can, however, draw
an entire group or family of curves with development as the
only variable factor. When this is done, we get a chart similar to the one in Figure 41. It shows the various gammas obtainable with a particular emulsion and a particular developer with different times of development.

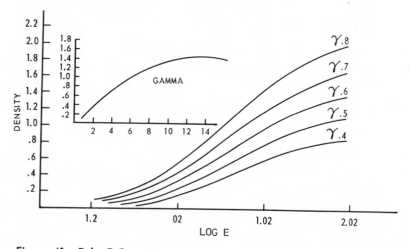

Figure 41   D logE Curve Variation Due to Increasing Developing Time

This chart, then, shows us the different possible contrasts that we can obtain when we change development time. To simplify the use of this information, we can construct a *time-gamma curve*. This curve plots all the information obtained from a family of curves into a single curve. It is constructed by plotting the gamma obtained on the vertical axis against the time of development on the horizontal axis. Such a curve constructed from the family of curves in the preceding diagram is shown in Figure 42.

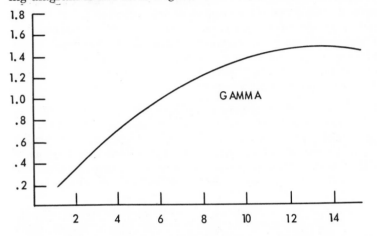

Figure 42   The Time-Gamma Curve From Curves in Figure 41

The advantage of a time-gamma curve is this. Assume we have a copy whose density range we can measure. Based on previous experience we have found that we get the best quality from negatives having a density range of 1.40 and, therefore, we want to produce a continuous-tone negative having this density range. We have read the density range of the copy and we know the desired density in our copy-negative. By substituting these two values in the formula

$$\gamma = \frac{\text{D.R. of negative}}{\text{D.R. of copy}}$$

we can obtain the value for the gamma necessary to produce this density range in our copy-negative. If we have a time-gamma curve available, we can draw a horizontal line from the value of the copy density range to where it intersects the time-gamma curve, and from this point drop a vertical line until it intersects the time axis. The value at this point would show us the necessary development time to produce the gamma we desire on the continuous-tone negative we are going to make.

47. THE DENSITOMETER

Now that we have discussed some of the terms, definitions, and equations that are used in densitometry, it is time to ask "How do we measure it?" The answer lies with the use of an instrument known as the densitometer. This instrument has a place where the tone area to be measured is positioned, a device or system for making either a direct density reading or a comparison between the tone area to be measured and a standard area, and a scale that will show the density reading as a numerical figure. There are two types of densitometers: the visual and the photoelectric.

47A. The Visual Densitometer. With a visual instrument, the tone area to be measured is placed in the path of a beam of light that passes through an eyepiece to one-half of a split viewing area. A second beam of light is sent into the other half of the split viewing field without going through the tone area. This second beam is sometimes called the control beam.

Figure 43　Typical Visual Densitometer

It is dimmed by a change in position until its visual appearance in the split field of the eyepiece seems to match the light intensity that is being transmitted through the sample being measured. In addition, a calibrated scale is attached to the control beam adjustment. When the visual appearance of both halves of the split field are the same, the density can be read from the scale.

47B. The Photoelectric Densitometer. The photoelectric instrument differs from the visual one in that a photoelectric cell is used to compare the tone area you are measuring with the control area. The cell is connected with a meter so that the density is read directly from the position of an indicating needle on the face of the meter. There is one big advantage

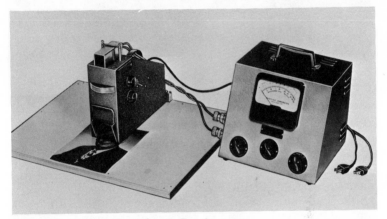

Figure 44   Typical Photoelectric Densitometer

of the photoelectric densitometer. A large number of density readings taken in rapid succession will not cause eye fatigue as may occur with the visual type of instrument. Eye fatigue can cause serious errors in judging the point where the light intensity of the two fields match. The result, then, may be incorrect density measurement.

47C. Transmission, Reflection and Combination Densitometers. Densitometers of either the visual or photoelectric type are built to read transmission density, reflection density, or both. In this last case, the instrument is known as a combination densitometer. In almost all cases, a combination densitometer is more expensive than one designed to read only reflection or transmission density.

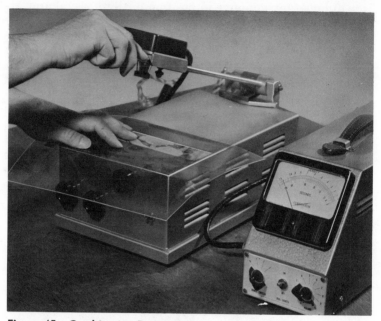

Figure 45   Combination Densitometer

For usual lithographic operations the scale of a transmission densitometer should cover a range of about 0.00 to 3.00 density units. When used for reflection density measurements, the scale should cover a range of 0.00 to 2.00 density units. The majority of all readings will fall within these limits. On most instruments, the size of the area that is read is approximately 5/32 of an inch in diameter. This area is large enough to cover a coarse-screen halftone image area, yet small enough to cover a uniform area on a continuous-tone negative or positive. For halftone work it should, however, be large enough to make an integrated density measurement; that is, one which includes several dots and the spaces between them.

48. THE PRACTICAL USE OF THE DENSITOMETER

The densitometer has definite practical value for the half-tone photographer. With it, and the intelligent use of densitometric principles, the photographer has an excellent working tool and a valuable control method. We cannot, in this space, cover all of the applications of a densitometer. However, certain important applications for the halftone photographer will be discussed. Many other applications are covered in the manuals supplied by the manufacturers of densitometers.

There are three specific applications of a densitometer which are of everyday value to the practical halftone photographer. These are:

1. As an instrument to calculate the evenness of illumination on the copyboard as well as at the focal plane.

2. To calculate filter factors.

3. As an exposure calculation device.

48A. Calculating Evenness of Illumination.

The photolithographer has two work areas where proper illumination is of extreme importance. These areas are the copyboard and the film plane. Most photographers, when setting the lights on their process cameras, make a specific effort to place the lights so that they illuminate the copyboard and the copy evenly. Their aim is to have the same amount of light falling on all areas of the copy. The photographer assumes that if the copy is evenly illuminated, then all areas of the negative that is being exposed will also be evenly illuminated. Unfortunately this is not the case.

The following diagram shows why this is wrong. Light rays from the outer edges of the copy have to travel farther than those which are on or closer to the optical axis of the lens. These same light rays also strike the emulsion at an angle and since they cover a greater area than those near the axis, their intensity is further diminished. Furthermore, lenses tend to vignette the light rays from the edges of the copy due to the barrel length, lens thickness, or both.

Thus, if the illumination at the focal plane is to be even, the edges of the copy must receive more light than the center of the copy. This is only one factor that tends to distort the reproduction of what otherwise might be evenly illuminated copy. Other factors are lens flare and internal reflections inside the camera bellows.

ILLUMINATION OF THE COPYBOARD. Here is a method of measuring, with the use of the densitometer, the intensity of light falling on the copyboard. For this operation it is necessary that the instrument have a photoelectric type head. The procedure is as follows:

Figure 46 Calculating the Illumination on the Copyboard

Set the camera at "same-size" with the arc lights placed in normal operating position.

Remove the head from the densitometer arm, and place it in the exact center of the copyboard with the photoelectric cell facing the lens.

Switch the densitometer scale to the lowest possible position to avoid burning out the meter when the arc lights are turned on. If the cell is ultra-sensitive, cover it with a few sheets of tissue or other material that will partially hold back the light.

Turn on the arc lights. Adjust the scale setting on the meter so that the meter will read mid-scale.

Record this meter reading.

Move the photoelectric cell to various positions on the copyboard, making certain that the cell faces the lens at all times. Record the position of the cell and the meter readings for each point.

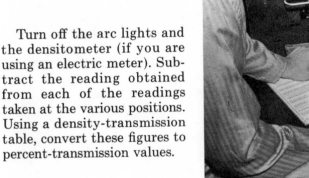

Turn off the arc lights and the densitometer (if you are using an electric meter). Subtract the reading obtained from each of the readings taken at the various positions. Using a density-transmission table, convert these figures to percent-transmission values.

The figures you have obtained will give you the relative percentage of light intensity at each point you have measured, assuming the central point to be 100 percent intensity.

The procedure described will enable you to determine the relative amount of light that is falling on various areas of your copyboard. In the event you desire, for some special reason, to illuminate your copyboard as evenly as possible, you can move the lights to more adequately compensate for the uneven illumination shown by the readings. Make a series of new readings, and repeat this procedure until the best possible condition is obtained. Special occasions may require an evenly illuminated copyboard. One such situation can occur when an extreme reduction of large copy is required. Here the copyboard is evenly illuminated for the image projected through the lens is so small that it can be considered as passing through the central portion of the lens alone.

EVEN ILLUMINATION AT THE FOCAL PLANE. A variation of the procedure in the preceding section will help you determine how even the illumination is which is falling upon the sensitive emulsion. Evenness of illumination here is a must. Proceed as follows:

1. Set the camera to "same-size" with the arc lights placed in your normal operating position.

Figure 47   Evenness of Illumination at Emulsion Plane

2. Although the ground glass can be used, it is best to use a clear piece of glass in the plate-holder bars.

3. Put a large sheet of even-toned white paper in the copyboard holder. The sheet should fill the entire copyboard area, or at least the area on which you wish to measure the variation of illumination. Paper of the cast-coated type is excellent for this purpose.

4. Remove the head from the densitometer arm, and place it in the exact center of the glass with the photoelectric cell facing the lens.

5. Switch the densitometer scale to the lowest possible position.

6. Turn on the arc lights.

7. Adjust the scale setting on the machine so that the meter will read mid-scale.

8. Record this meter reading.

9. Move the photoelectric cell to various positions on the glass surface, making certain that the cell faces the lens at all times.

10. Record the position of the cell and the meter readings for each point.

11. Turn off the arc lights and the densitometer. Subtract the reading taken at Step 8 from each of the readings taken at the various positions. Using a density-transmission table, convert these figures to percent-transmission figures.

The figures you have obtained will give you the relative percentage of light intensity reaching the film plane at each of the points you have measured, assuming the central point to be of 100 percent intensity.

As with the previous procedure your lights can then be moved to obtain more even illumination at the film plane. In both these procedures, the camera was set at "same-size." This was done for the simple reason that it is the most frequently used size in lithographic camera operation. In the event your own operations call for another scale setting more frequently, then the camera can be set at this position for the readings.

Here is a hint that will save time: Mark the values obtained directly on the glass surface with a grease pencil. Then, when repeat readings are made after a change of light position, a direct comparison can be made with the previous readings with no need to consult an additional information sheet.

48B. Determining Filter Factors. There are three methods that can be used with a densitometer to measure filter factors. The first two methods will give a close approximation quickly. The third, however, will give accurate determinations.

Most densitometers are sold with three color filters attached to the densitometer head. These are slid into position when making color measurements. They are also used when making the necessary measurements to determine filter factors.

The simplest method is to place the filter under the densitometer head and make a direct density reading. This figure when converted to *"percent transmission"* with the use of density-transmission tables will give the amount of light transmitted by the filter. To convert this figure to a filter factor (f. f.) substitute this value in the following equation:

$$f.\,f. = \frac{100}{\%\text{ transmission}}$$

Thus, in the case of a filter that transmitted 50 percent of the light incident upon it, the factor would be:

$$f.\,f. = \frac{100}{50} = 2$$

In the case of a filter that transmitted 18 percent of the light incident upon it, the factor would be:

$$f.\,f. = \frac{100}{18} = 5.6 \text{ (to the nearest tenth)}$$

When the filter is to be used with a panchromatic emulsion, the photoelectric cell of the densitometer is used without any of the color filters mounted in the head. Thus, the filter is being measured for its effect upon white light. Although not fully accurate, this simulates the wide color sensitivity of the panchromatic emulsion.

For the same reason, when the filter being measured is to be used with orthochromatic film, the reading is taken through the green filter on the densitometer. Light through this filter roughly approximates the color sensitivity of ortho emulsions.

Finally, if the filter is for use with the blue-sensitive or color-blind emulsions, make the reading through the blue filter on the densitometer head.

Caution: These are rough measurements and will only give an approximate value for the filter factor. A photoelectric densitometer is specified because it is almost impossible to match the two different-colored fields that occur in the split-field finder of a visual instrument. This is due to the fact that the filter being measured is inserted into the optical path of the instrument.

The second method is a variation of the one just discussed. In this method, the scale of the densitometer is set to zero when the photoelectric head is placed on the ground glass of the camera. White light is allowed to enter the lens. The filter to be measured is then placed in the Waterhouse-stop slot of the lens, and a new reading is taken. This reading is converted to percent-transmission figures and the remainder of the procedure is the same as for the method described previously. As before, the densitometer's color filters are used to simulate the effect of the filter being checked on the various types of emulsions.

The third method of obtaining filter factors is an accurate one, although it takes considerably longer to do. Briefly it is this: A gray scale is photographed on a film or plate without a filter. The filter whose factor you wish to determine is inserted into the lens. On a second film or plate expose the gray scale again for the same exposure time. After the two shots are processed, read the densities of the highlight steps of both scales. Now compute the exposure that would be required to bring the density of the highlight step on the second scale to the same density as the original scale. The two exposures that will create the equal densities are then used in the following formula:

$$f.\,f. = \frac{\text{filtered light exposure}}{\text{white light exposure}}$$

For example, suppose that an exposure of 150 seconds to white light produced a satisfactory negative on an ortho film. The same emulsion and the same exposure were then used with a yellow (Wratten #8) filter. The result showed that the exposure necessary to produce the same density in the highlight step would have to be 222 seconds. Substituting in the formula, we have:

$$f.\,f. = \frac{222}{150} = 1.48$$

Thus, the filter factor for the Wratten #8 filter with the particular ortho film that was used is 1.48. The only point in this procedure that has not been explained is how to calculate the correct exposure necessary to obtain a given density. This will be covered in the section that follows.

48C. Exposure Calculation. As a starting point, let us read the densities of each step of a gray scale. In addition, let us make a continuous-tone negative of this scale that is a good reproduction of the original. If you are not certain what a good continuous-tone negative is, make a negative to a gamma of 1.00. Assume that the exposure was 58 seconds at an aperture of f45. Now, let us read the densities of each of the steps on this negative that we have produced by trial-and-error procedure. The original scale and the negative that was made of it are the control for the procedure we are about to describe.

We now take a new piece of copy. Let's say that the highlight area of this new copy has a density of 0.46 as compared to the density of 0.10 on the control scale. However, we wish the negative density to be the same (1.68) as was produced by the control scale. We can tell by inspection that we need a longer exposure to make the negative density high enough, but the question is — how much more exposure do we need?

You can determine this with the density measurements you made, as follows:

1. Using the density-transmission chart, determine the percent of transmission for both of the highlight areas. In this case the values would be:

0.10 = 79.43% transmission
0.46 = 34.67% transmission

2. Substitute these values plus the original exposure in the following formula:

$$\text{Required Exposure (R.E.)} = \frac{\text{original exposure} \times \text{original \% transmission}}{\text{new \% transmission}}$$

$$\text{R.E.} = \frac{58 \times 79.43}{34.67}$$

R.E. = 133 seconds (approximately)

This, then, is the procedure and formula for finding the necessary exposure to produce a desired density value once a control has been established.

To adapt this continuous-tone procedure to halftone work, proceed as follows:

Shoot a halftone negative (having as complete a tone range as possible) from the original gray scale. Note the original gray scale densities and the halftone dots they produced with this test exposure. When a new copy is received for shooting, pick the key area of the copy and determine what dot size is desired in this area. Find this dot size on the halftone control negative, and locate the original gray scale density that produced it. Then substitute these values in the formula as before. Of course, now the formula will read in "% reflectance" rather than "% transmission" as we are dealing with the reflection densities from the original gray scale and the copy rather than the transmission density of negatives.

Chapter XIII

SPECIAL PROCESSING PROCEDURES IN MAKING HALFTONES

The photographic process depends not only on the action of light, but also on various chemical actions and reactions that take place in the light-sensitive emulsion. All negatives are not always perfect, and with the various chemical techniques described in this chapter, the effect of light on the emulsion can be chemically modified to produce an end-result that more closely meets the photographic requirements. With the proper use of various chemical processes, the photographic negative can be lightened or darkened. This produces the equivalent effect of subtracting or adding additional exposures at a different time than when the exposure was actually made.

49. ETCHING AND CHEMICAL REDUCTION

The desire of every halftone photographer is to produce negatives and positives that are of excellent quality and can be used without any additional work being done on them. It sometimes happens, however, that a halftone or continuous-tone negative does not meet the standards. Rather than spend the time necessary to make another shot, it is sometimes possible to "save" the film or plate by the use of a reducing solution, which reduces the density of the silver deposits on the emulsion. This process is known as "etching" when the work is done on a halftone image, and as "reduction" when it is done on a continuous-tone image. At other times, etching or reduction can be done to produce a desired effect.

In using this procedure, the photographer mixes a reducing solution, and then gives the negative or positive a "bite," "etch," or "cut." These terms refer to the actual operation of reduction. A "flat bite" consists of inserting the entire sensitive emulsion into a reducing solution at one time. When the reduction has progressed far enough, the film is removed and washed. This completes the operation.

When giving the emulsion a "local bite," the photographer applies the reducing solution directly on a small portion of emulsion which has to be reduced. This is done with a wad of cotton, or with an artist's brush which has been dipped into the reducing solution. When the action has progressed sufficiently, the reduction is stopped with a wad of cotton saturated with water or hypo (depending upon the reducing agent being used), or the entire film is immersed into a water bath.

The most common reducer is a solution known as "Farmer's reducer." It is most often used in the form of a flat etch to remove the slight veiling or fog that occurs in the shadow areas of halftone negatives. This operation is performed by dipping the film or plate in the reducing solution for 5 to 60 seconds depending upon the amount of veiling present.

When continuous-tone negatives are shot as the intermediate step towards the production of a final halftone image, they must occasionally be reduced. Although Farmer's reducer can be used for this operation, other reducers which act differently may be prepared. These reducers are of three different types depending upon the way that they react with the silver image. They are known as subtractive, proportional, or super-proportional reducers.

49A. The Physical Action of Reduction. The physical action that seems to take place in reduction is as follows: When the reducer contacts the gelatin surface, the solution penetrates evenly over all the areas whether they are opaque or transparent. Upon contacting the upper surface of the dot, reduction of silver takes place almost immediately. The reaction products produced at this top surface dilute the fresh reducer as it penetrates into the top surface of the dot. This causes the action that is taking place to become less vigorous. Meanwhile, the reducer that penetrates into the clear gelatin starts to attack the side surfaces of the dot. The reaction products created at this surface continue to fall downward toward the base of the emulsion and fresh reducer continues to attack the sides of the dot as it diffuses into position. Thus, the circulatory motion that takes place at the side of the dot is more vigorous than the one at the top surface. Because the reducing action is replenished more rapidly on the side surfaces, the reducing action takes place more quickly and with a greater effect on the sides of the dot than on the top. The effect, therefore, is to reduce the diameter of the dot more rapidly than its height. The following illustration shows this action.

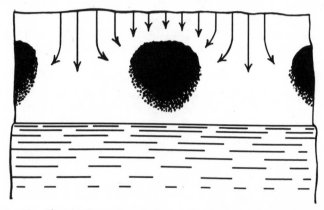

Figure 48   Sketch Illustrating Action of the Reducer During Dot-Etching

49B. Subtractive Reducers. Subtractive reducers act by removing equal quantities of silver from all areas of the image. This has the effect of reducing the lighter image areas more than the areas of heavier density. On a photographic negative, this means that the shadow portions of the image are reduced more rapidly than the highlight areas. Some examples of subtractive reducers follow.

FARMER'S REDUCER. Farmer's reducer is a mixture of potassium ferricyanide and hypo. This mixture is relatively unstable, and the longer it stands the weaker it becomes. It can, however, be used as a two-step operation, first applying the hypo solution, then the ferricyanide solution, and then the hypo once more. This can be continued in a like manner until the required amount of reduction is obtained. When used in a one-step procedure, the two stock solutions are mixed and used immediately.

FARMER'S REDUCER FORMULA:

	Metric Units	U. S. Units
Stock Solution A:		
Potassium Ferricyanide	300 grams	12 oz.
Water	700 cc.	27 oz.
Stock Solution B:		
Hypo, crystal	1000 grams	2 lbs.
Water	880 cc.	27 oz.
(Adjust to 35° Baumé by adding hypo or water as required)		
Working Solution: Solution A		1 part
Solution B		10 parts
Water		10 parts

IODINE-CYANIDE REDUCER. The iodine-cyanide reducer is an old one that was standard back in the days of wet plate photography. It is, however, extremely effective. One problem associated with its use is its toxicity. *Cyanides are POISONOUS.* They are not only deadly when taken internally, but their fumes are dangerous when inhaled over prolonged periods of time. Cyanides are absorbed slowly through the skin, and rapidly through breaks in the skin. Although potentially dangerous, they can be handled safely when proper precautions are taken. In the event this solution is used, make certain that all bottles containing cyanides are marked POISON.

IODINE-CYANIDE REDUCER FORMULA:

	Metric Units	U. S. Units
Stock Solution A:		
Iodine, re-sublimed	14 grams	1/2 oz.
Potassium Iodide, C. P.	28 grams	1 oz.
Water, to make	1000 cc.	1 qt.
(Add a small quantity of water to the chemicals, and after the iodine is completely dissolved, add the remaining water)		
Stock Solution B:		
Sodium Cyanide	85 grams	3 oz.
Water, to make	887 cc.	30 oz.
Working Solution: Solution A		1 part
Solution B		2 parts
Water		16 parts

Note: The metric and U. S. formulas are independent. Quantities listed under them are not interchangeable.

CERIC SULFATE REDUCER. Ceric sulfate is the only practical dot-etching agent that will keep indefinitely. The extent of exhaustion of the solution can be determined readily by the color. Any sediment that is formed does no harm. Either anhydrous ceric sulfate or ceric bisulfate may be used to prepare a stock solution. However, a 2 percent sulfuric acid solution must be used for diluting it to working strength or to stop the action of the reducer.

CERIC SULFATE STOCK SOLUTION
(from anhydrous ceric sulfate)

	Metric Units	U. S. Units
Ceric Sulfate, anhydrous	67 grams	2 3/8 oz.
Sulfuric Acid, Conc. (sp. gr. 1.84)	28 cc.	1 oz.
Water, to make	1000 cc.	1 qt.

CERIC SULFATE STOCK SOLUTION
(from ceric bisulfate)

Ceric Bisulfate	67 grams	2 3/8 oz.
Sulfuric Acid (sp. gr. 1.84)	20 cc.	325 minims
Water, to make	1000 cc.	1 qt.

Weigh the ceric sulfate or ceric bisulfate into a beaker, add the sulfuric acid and mix thoroughly, then add 1 ounce of water. Heat, add more water, and continue heating and adding water in small quantities until the solid salt is completely dissolved and the orange-yellow solution becomes clear. Transfer the solution to a suitable graduate and make up the final volume by adding water which is at room temperature.

SULFURIC ACID STOCK SOLUTION
(2 percent by volume)

	Metric Units	U. S. Units
Water	1000 cc.	1 qt.
Sulfuric Acid (sp. gr. 1.84)	20 cc.	5/8 oz.

(Add the acid slowly to the water stirring continuously. Never add the water to the acid as this may produce violent spattering.)

To use:

As a tray etching solution:

Ceric Sulfate Stock Solution	1 part
Sulfuric Acid Solution, 2%	3 parts

As a local etching solution:
  Ceric Sulfate Stock Solution   1 part
  Sulfuric Acid Solution, 2%   1 part

To stop reduction:
  The action of the ceric sulfate may be stopped by
  washing the film with water, although a 2 percent sulfuric acid solution is preferable. Allowance must be
  made for a certain amount of continuing action.

49C. Proportional Reducers. A reducer of this type is normally
used to reduce continuous-tone negatives or positives. Its
action is such that it removes the silver in proportion to the
amount present. In other words, the greater the density, the
greater the reduction. Its widest use is in correcting negatives
that have been properly exposed but overdeveloped. A typical formula follows:

PERSULFATE-PERMANGANATE REDUCER

Solution A:	Metric Units	U. S. Units
Water	1000 cc.	32 oz.
Potassium Permanganate	0.3 gram	4 grains
Sulfuric Acid (10% solution)	16 cc.	1/2 oz.
Solution B:		
Water	3000 cc.	96 oz.
Ammonium Persulfate	90 grams	3 oz.
Working Solution:		
Solution A		1 part
Solution B		3 parts

After reduction, clear negatives in 1% solution of sodium
bisulfite and wash thoroughly.

SULFURIC ACID SOLUTION
(10 percent by volume)

	Metric Units	U. S. Units
Water	1000 cc.	1 qt.
Sulfuric Acid (sp. gr. 1.84)	92.5 cc.	3 1/8 oz.

  Add the acid slowly to the water, stirring continuously.
  Never add the water to the acid as this may produce
  violent spattering.

SUPER-PROPORTIONAL REDUCER. This reducer, as with all
proportional-type reducers, used on continuous-tone negatives or positives, acts in the reverse manner as a subtractive

reducer. It attacks the darkest portions of the image first. This is the highlight area of the negative. The reducer has the effect of flattening the tonal scale. It is used on over-developed negatives of contrasty subjects. A typical formula follows:

PERSULFATE REDUCER FORMULA

Stock Solution:	Metric Units	U. S. Units
Water	1000 cc.	32 oz.
Ammonium Persulfate	60 grams	2 oz.
Sulfuric Acid, C. P.	3 cc.	3/4 dram
Working Solution:		
Stock Solution		1 part
Water		2 parts

After reduction, immerse in acid fixing bath for a few moments before washing.

49D. Intensification. There will be occasions where density will have to be added to the photographic image. This can be done by a procedure known as *intensification.* The intensifying solution adds a chromium, mercury, or silver compound to the black metallic silver image in the negative or positive. These opaque compounds increase the density of the silver image.

A continuous-tone silver image adapts fairly well to chemical intensification. However, the intensification of a halftone image on a usual lith-type emulsion is very limited. The dot size can be increased only a small percent and there are dangers of chemical staining that can make the halftone image useless. It is a process that does not lend itself to continuous build-up of an image. And, in general, is used as little as possible. The two intensifiers that are given use mercury and chromium compounds. The mercury compound will give a higher degree of intensification although the solution is not as permanent as the one made with chromium.

MERCURY INTENSIFIER[1].

MERCURY INTENSIFIER FORMULA

Bleach Solution:	Metric Units	U. S. Units
Potassium Bromide	22.5 grams	3/4 av. oz.
Mercuric Chloride	22.5 grams	3/4 av. oz.
Water, to make	1.0 liter	32 liq. oz.

---

(1) *Formulas for the Graphic Arts,* Eastman Kodak Company, Rochester, N. Y.

Bleach the negative in the above solution until it is white, then wash thoroughly. After bleaching, the negative can be blackened with: (1) A 10 percent sulfite solution; (2) A developing solution such as Kodak D-72 diluted 1 to 2; or (3) Dilute ammonia (1 part 28 percent concentrated ammonia to 9 parts water). These give progressively greater density in the order named. After re-development, the negative is washed and dried. The process can be repeated if necessary.

CHROMIUM INTENSIFIER[1].

CHROMIUM INTENSIFIER FORMULA

Stock Solution:

	Metric Units	U. S. Units
Potassium Bichromate	90 grams	3 av. oz.
Hydrochloric Acid Conc.	64 cc.	2 liq. oz.
Water, to make	1.0 liter	32 liq. oz.

For use: Dilute one part of stock solution with ten parts of water. After bleaching in the above solution, wash thoroughly and re-develop for about ten minutes in a developer such as D-72 which does not contain a high concentrate of sulfite. After re-developing, rinse, fix, and wash thoroughly.

49E. Special Hardener — For after-treatment of films and plates[2]. This formula is recommended for the treatment of negatives or positives which normally would be softened by chemical treatments such as for the removal of stains, intensification or reduction. This can be used for either continuous-tone or halftone emulsions.

SPECIAL HARDENER FORMULA

	Metric Units	U. S. Units
Water	500 cc.	16 liq. oz.
Formalin[3]	10 cc.	2 1/2 drams
Sodium Carbonate, Monohydrated	6.0 grams	90 grains
Water, to make	1.0 liter	32 liq. oz.

After hardening in the above solution for 3 minutes, negatives should be rinsed and immersed for 5 minutes in a fresh, acid fixing bath and then washed thoroughly before they are given any further chemical treatments.

---

(1) *Processing Chemicals and Formulas for Black and White Photography,* Eastman Kodak Company, Rochester, N. Y., 1954.

(2) *Formulas for the Graphic Arts,* Eastman Kodak Company, Rochester, N. Y.

(3) Formalin is a 40% solution of formaldehyde. This is approximately a 37% solution by weight.

Chapter XIV

THE PROCESS LENS

The photographic lens is a light modulator. Before any proper consideration can be given to an instrument that alters something, the material or phenomenon that is being altered should be explained sufficiently so that its basic properties are understood. For this reason, prior to a discussion of lenses, we will briefly examine the nature and properties of light.

50. THE NATURE OF LIGHT

Light is a form of radiant energy that is capable of affecting the human eye in such a manner as to produce vision. There has been a tremendous amount of work done on light, both theoretical and experimental. But, even though something is understood of how it is produced and propagated, its true nature still remains unknown.

The ancient Greeks thought that light was made up of a stream of corpuscles. Sir Isaac Newton (1643-1727) developed a corpuscular theory of light which held that light consisted of a hail of separate particles. Huygens (1629-1695) proposed a wave theory of light, but the established standing of Newton's scientific authority prevented the acceptance of any theory other than Newton's corpuscular theory. However, about 1800, Young (1773-1829) and Fresnel (1788-1827) carefully looked at the problem again. They were able to explain certain phenomena with the wave theory that could not be reconciled with the corpuscular theory of Newton. However, even this did not stop the search for more information about light. In 1873, Maxwell (1831-1879) proposed an elaborate electromagnetic theory of light. This was not the complete answer either. To explain still other phenomena, Planck (1858-1947) developed the quantum theory which is an elaborate version of a corpuscular-type theory.

This leaves us with two basically contradictory theories, the wave theory and the quantum theory. The modern physicist is left to his own choice as to which theory fits best the phenomena he wishes to explain. It is fortunate, in considering the action of a lens, that we can use the simple wave theory of light. As a matter of fact, the statement that light will travel in a straight line within a continuous medium is a true enough approximation to allow us to use this statement for various applications concerning lenses.

51. LIGHT SOURCES

The most common source of light with which we are familiar is the sun. However, in process photography we also make use of incandescent lamps, arc lights, fluorescent lamps, and the recently introduced pulsed xenon arc.

The incandescent lamp is basically a glass bulb enclosing a conducting metal filament that is heated to the point where it emits light.

The arc lamp consists of a pair of carbon rods connected in a series circuit with a resistance across an electric power supply. As was mentioned previously, the arc formed between the carbons is caused by the burning gases given off by the carbons when the current is on. The majority of the light that is radiated comes from the crater formed in the tips of the carbons. The type of light emitted depends on the materials put in the core of the carbon rods.

The fluorescent lamp consists of a glass tube containing a gas and having fluorescent material coated on the interior wall. When an electrical charge is dissipated through the gas, it energizes the fluorescent material causing it to give off light.

The pulsed xenon arc (PXA) lamp is a development of the General Electric Company that combines the features of the high power "flash" of a flash lamp and an approximately steady light source. In operation, these xenon gas-filled quartz tubes pulsate 120 times each second. Each pulse sets off a flash of one-thousandth of a second duration. The speed of these continuous flashes gives the appearance of a steady light source, although a slight flicker is noticeable.

52. REFRACTION

When a light wave falls on the surface between two different mediums or materials at an angle other than 90°, the light wave will change its direction in the second medium. The direction taken will depend upon the speed (velocity) of light in the two mediums. Here, for the sake of convenience, it is simpler to think in terms of a ray of light rather than a wave front. When the velocity of a ray is reduced, it will change direction toward the normal (a line perpendicular to the surface). When the velocity of a ray is increased, it will change direction away from the normal.

52A. The Law of Refraction. The above statements make up a rule which is known as the Law of Refraction. It can be written as a formula as follows:

$$\frac{\text{sine } i}{\text{sine } r} = \frac{V_1}{V_2} \quad (1)$$

where V_1 and V_2 are the velocities in the two mediums. Figure 49 shows the effect of refraction.

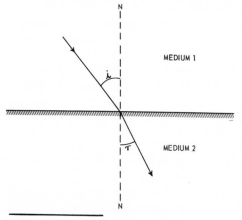

MEDIUM 1

MEDIUM 2

Figure 49 Refraction of Light

(1) Sine—a mathematical term used in calculating angles and sides of triangles where one of the angles is a right angle (90°).

In a right-angle triangle, the sine of any angle (except the right angle) can be determined by dividing the length of the side opposite the angle to be measured by the hypotenuse (the side opposite the right angle). In the following figure, the sine of the (angle "Q" is equal to $\frac{A}{C}$.)

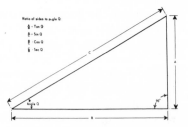

52B. The Index of Refraction. The ratio of the velocity of the light in a vacuum to the velocity of the light in the medium it is entering is known as the *index of refraction*. The following shows the index of refraction for certain materials:

INDEX OF REFRACTION

Air	1.0003
Alcohol	1.36
Canada Balsam	1.52
Diamond	2.47
Glass, Crown	1.52
Glass, Flint	1.54-1.94
Water	1.33

There is a wide range of refractive indexes for various types of glass. Lens designers use this knowledge and with various curvatures and combinations of types of glass build a lens which is designed to do a particular type of job.

53. THE PROCESS LENS

The process lens is designed to do a specific job. It is designed for line, halftone, and color photography over a range from 20 percent reduction to 200 percent magnification. However, the majority of work is usually shot at same-size or close to it. The maximum aperture of a process lens is small in comparison to conventional photographic lenses.

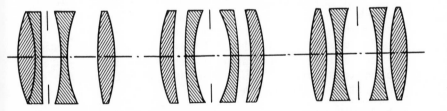

Figure 50   Some Typical Lens Constructions

Usually it is somewhere around f9. A symmetrical type of construction is favored due to the type of distortion that would adversely affect a process image. Typical constructions employed in a process lens are shown in Figure 50.

The greater the number of air-to-glass surfaces in the lens, the more likelihood that the stray light internally reflected within the lens will cause a decrease in contrast. For example, Kingslake[1] has shown the following percentages of stray light in lenses with the listed number of air-to-glass surfaces:

Number of Air-to-Glass Surfaces	Percent Stray Light
2	0.23
4	1.16
6	2.50
8	4.03

For this reason, Kingslake states, "... for photographing black lines on a white ground, ... it is likely that clearer reproduction might be obtained if a lens having fewer glass-to-air surfaces such as the Dagor were used."[2]

54. LENS ABERRATIONS

The process lens must be, and usually is, designed for a minimum of aberrations. Straight lines must be reproduced as straight lines, and colors must all come to a focus at the same point. These are but two types of aberrations for which a process lens is specially corrected.

The lens aberrations discussed below are typical faults that can be found in poorly designed lenses. However, these discussions are supplied as background information only, for most aberrations are non-existent or of minor significance in any good process lens. In the process lens supplied by any reputable manufacturer, distortion, spherical aberration, and coma are non-existent from the point of view of the photographer who is using the lens. There are traces of astigmatism or curvature of field in many process lenses, but they are of minor consequence. With this in mind, let us discuss the lens aberrations included here.

54A. Distortion. The image magnification of a lens having distortion will vary depending upon its distance from the axis of the lens. If the magnification at the edge of the field is greater than at the center, we get a positive type of distortion known as "pin-cushion" distortion. When the magnification at the center of the image is greater than at the edge of the field, a negative type of distortion known as "barrel'" dis-

---

(1) R. Kingslake, "The Optics of Photographic Lenses," *Handbook of Photography,* Henney and Dudley (Editors), McGraw-Hill, N. Y., 1939, page 22.

(2) R. Kingslake, "The Development of Photographic Objective," *Handbook of Photography,* Henney and Dudley (Editors), McGraw-Hill, N. Y., 1939, page 48.

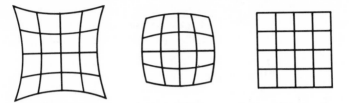

Figure 51   Pin-Cushion and Barrel Distortion of Square Copy

tortion is produced. Both types of this distortion are shown in Figure 51.

The location of the lens diaphragm can be another cause of distortion. When the diaphragm is placed in front of the lens, barrel distortion results; with the diaphragm behind the lens, pin-cushion distortion results. This aberration is avoided with the proper choice of lens elements and diaphragm position. Distortion could be a very serious aberration fault in any lens used to produce plates or films on which accurate measurements had to be made.

54B. Spherical Aberration. If this type of aberration is present, the light rays passing through the marginal area (rim) of the lens come to a focus at a different point than the rays passing through the center of the lens. This means that there is no single point of focus. The distortion is measured as the distance along the axis of the lens separating the points where the marginal and central rays come to focus. Stopping down the lens tends to eliminate some of the marginal rays and helps to reduce this aberration.

54C. Chromatic Aberration. If a lens is uncorrected or only partially corrected for chromatic aberration, its index of refraction will vary with the wavelength (color) of the light. A lens with this fault separates the various colored components of light in such a way that, when they emerge from the final

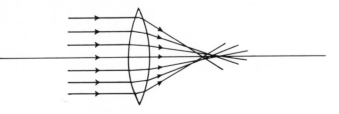

Figure 52   Spherical Aberration

surface of the lens, the different colors come to a focus at different points. Modern process lenses from any reputable manufacturer are always corrected for chromatic aberration.

54D. Coma. Coma results if the various circular zones of the lens produce different magnifications. The greater the angle between the object and the lens, the greater this fault could be. The image formed is sharp at the center, but has an indistinct edge, giving a tail-like (comet) effect. This aberration is usually present along with other aberrations so that the viewer will rarely, if ever, see a pure comatic aberration.

54E. Astigmatism. A lens which is astigmatic will not form a sharp image of lines at right angles to each other except in the center of the field. For example, when the horizontal lines are in focus, the vertical lines are not. It can readily be understood why an aberration of this type cannot be tolerated in a lens for process work.

54F. Curvature of Field. If the axial rays are brought to a focus closer to the lens than the marginal rays, a line connecting all these focal points will be found to have a generally curved shape. If a straight line is photographed with a lens having this aberration, the effect would be a sharp image in the center of the line, gradually going out of focus as we move along the line a greater and greater angular distance from the axis of the lens.

54G. Aberrations and Lens Design. In any lens a certain amount of aberrations are present. The lens designer tries to eliminate most of them, partially correct others, and balance the remaining aberrations by the proper choice of glass types,

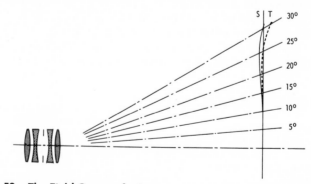

Figure 53   The Field Curves of a Lens

lens element curvature, number of lens elements, aperture position, and other design factors. When a lens is designed for a specific purpose, the lens designer determines the aberrations that would cause the greatest problem during use and then tries to minimize them. Sometimes this has to be done at the expense of not fully correcting other aberrations. However, at no time does he allow any aberration to become objectionable.

55. IMAGE DISTORTION

Even though a lens may be thoroughly corrected for aberrations, there are circumstances which still cause a distortion of the image. The most serious distortions are those that are caused by the camera being out-of-square. This can occur from improper installation, vibration causing a change in the relative positions of the camera components, and various other factors.

The simplest method of recognizing distortion due to an out-of-square camera is the so-called "keystone" effect that is produced when projecting a square image. If a perfectly square copy were put into the copyboard of a misaligned or vibrating camera and photographed, the image reproduced would have lines that are straight, but not parallel to each other. This creates a keystone image on the film being exposed.

Certain faults that cause this effect can be corrected by the photographer. For example, he might tilt the lens flange to rectify the fault. However, if the heavy units of the camera are out of alignment, a competent mechanic from the manufacturer or supplier should be called in. Vibration from heavy machinery in the plant may cause the camera parts to get out of alignment. Yet, the actual misalignment may be too small for the photographer to measure and correct accurately. Skilled camera mechanics have the tools and measuring instruments to detect this condition and make recommendations for eliminating it.

56. LENS RESOLUTION

The resolving power of a lens is its ability to produce separate images of objects that are very close together. This means that if two point sources of light were brought closer and closer together while being viewed through a lens, a point would be reached where they would blend into one another and no longer be distinguishable as separate light sources. At this point, the resolving power of the lens is said to have been reached. Additional magnification of the images would not help, as the size of the spots would increase at the same rate as their separation, and the resolving power would remain the same.

Resolving power is determined for photographic emulsions as well as photographic lenses. It usually is stated as a numerical value equal to the number of lines per millimeter that can be recorded by an emulsion as separate, distinct, unblurred lines.

When an image of a point source of light is formed by a perfect lens, we find that the image is not a true point, but rather a tiny disk of light that has a number of faint rings of light surrounding it. This image is called an *airy disk*. The diameter of the disk's central portion is extremely small. Thus, even when two such disks are resolved, the figure is so small that the grain of the normal photographic plate is larger than the separation between the two point sources. Consequently this phenomenon rarely enters into photographic calculations in lithography.

The faint rings around the airy disk are actually diffraction effects, and they gradually disappear as the lens aperture is made larger. However, as the aperture of the lens is widened, other aberrations of the lens become more prominent. Therefore, when maximum sharpness is desired from a lens, the aperture must be opened to a point where it is large enough to minimize diffraction effects, yet small enough to keep the normal lens aberrations from affecting the quality of the image. For this reason the maximum sharpness is obtained when a lens is stopped down somewhere between its widest and its smallest apertures. With process lenses, this is usually an aperture of approximately f22.

As used in the lithographic industry, the term "resolving" power is not used in its true sense. Rather, we use it to indicate the ability of a lens to record fine detail. If we apply this interpretation, what we are actually doing is discussing the "sharpness" of the lens.

57. FLARE

Flare is unwanted light that is spread over the projected image from various sources. For example, lens flare would be the unwanted light that is spread over the image from the many internal reflections within the lens. These reflections occur at the internal-glass surfaces of the lens where they contact another medium such as air. In addition, we have camera flare. This occurs within the bellows of the camera. The light passing through the camera strikes the bellows and sidewalls and, in reflecting off, causes the unwanted light to strike the sensitive emulsion. There are also other forms of flare. One is caused by a very bright light, like the sun, shining directly into a lens. Another type is caused by light striking scratches in the filters that are being used. Other types of flare are caused by reflections of light from the copyboard, and from dust that is in the air or which has settled on the various elements of the camera and lens.

The problem of flare is of extreme importance to the halftone photographer. That this problem is a common one is well known among the technical men in the industry. However, the effects of flare are not well known among photographers. Many of them are totally unaware of the problem. They are, therefore, unaware of the increased quality they could obtain if they were to limit the amount of flare present in their equipment.

Why Flare Is Important. What does flare do that makes it so important to us? In the first place we must remember that the flare causes an additional exposure which is not under the photographer's control. As such, it gives the effect of a small fogging exposure, or something similar to a short flash exposure. When making line shots, the additional flare exposure can plug up the fine lines which would normally be kept open. The halftone photographer will find that flare causes a loss of contrast in the shadow areas of halftone negatives and that he cannot get enough contrast when shooting from poor copy. One additional fault, which is due to flare, is the flattening of detail in halftone positives made from continuous-tone negatives. The point is that we lose detail and contrast when we permit this fault — flare — to go uncorrected.

Perhaps you will wonder why this emphasis on flare was not always pronounced, or why it was not considered important before. Flare always has been of great importance, but the average photographer knew little or nothing about it. He adapted himself to the conditions that existed with the equipment that he was operating. If dirt in the lens was causing flare, if there was flare coming from the copyboard, if internal reflections within the bellows were causing this condition, he did the best he could without realizing that the reduction of flare would have given him superior results, and that he need not have operated under the handicap which flare creates.

To give you some idea of how much flare can be present and the tolerances that are acceptable, here is a quotation from a report by J. A. C. Yule[1]:

"With an uncoated lens, under good conditions with proper precautions, the flare should not be above 2.5 percent. If the proper precautions are not taken — the lens gets dirty for instance, or stray light shines into the lens — it may rise to as much as 7 percent. In one instance it was actually 13 percent. With a coated lens, the flare can be reduced to less than 0.5 percent. For example, when one lens was re-polished, surface-treated, and the edges blackened, the flare was reduced from about 8.0 to 0.4 percent."

Not only is flare present within the camera and the lens, but the size of the copy and the percentage of white area can also help to produce it. Increasing the size of the copy and thus increasing the total amount of white surface that will reflect light will also increase flare. In addition, with a given-size copy, putting additional white surface around it, such as a border, will increase the flare.

If you had a camera set up with a minimum amount of flare present, and then were able to suddenly increase the amount of flare, the most noticeable effect would be the sudden change in the exposure and development times necessary to produce a satisfactory negative or positive. The exposure would drop to as much as one-sixth its former value while, at the same time, the development might have to be increased over two times to compensate for the flattening effect of the overall unwanted flare exposure. Under a condition of minimum flare, the normal exposure times would have to be increased to produce an improvement in dot quality and shadow detail. In many shops the exposure is already too long. Shop conditions exist where a 20- to 30-minute exposure is not uncommon. Under these conditions a certain controlled amount of flare may prove to be an advantage. However, the flare that is obtained from internal lens surfaces, internal camera surfaces, light reflections, or white copy is largely uncontrol-

---

(1) J. A. C. Yule, "Lens Flare in Process Cameras," TAGA, *1st Annual Proceedings*, Chicago, Illinois, April 1949.

lable. If necessary, a reasonable amount of flare can be introduced into the exposure system in a controlled manner by the use of a flash lamp. Certainly, the tremendous advantage of this method, which is under the photographer's control, cannot be overemphasized.

TESTING FOR FLARE. In the previously mentioned article by Yule, he suggests a method of testing for flare. The materials needed are a square piece of gray paper with a 50 percent reflectance[1]. The paper should be a square whose sides are equal to the focal length of the lens that is being used for the test. In addition, a white strip and a black strip about 2 x 10 inches are needed. Make the black strip from an old black lacquered ferrotype tin to give you the darkest possible black. A special film gray scale, calibrated as follows, will complete the test materials. Take any film step tablet and read the densities of each step on a densitometer. Convert these density figures to "percent transmission." Subtract 0.1 from each of these transmission values. (The 0.1 figure corresponds to the reflectance of the black strip.) You now have a calibrated gray scale that can be read directly as "percent flare."

The LTF recommended system of measuring lens flare rates the percent image contrast to that of the original. The test method is as follows:

---

(1) Section 47 in Chapter XII describes the instruments and techniques for making and handling such measurements as reflectance and transmittance.

Figure 54   Lens Flare Test

Cut a transparent gray scale (such as the Eastman Kodak Step Tablet #2) in half to make two identical 1/2″ wide scales. Call these A and B.

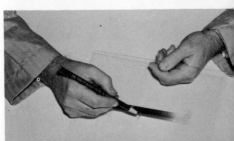

On one scale, A, mark the step closest to a density of 2.0. Tape this half of the scale onto the center of a piece of 8″ x 10″ clear glass.

Figure 54 Lens Flare Test (continued)

Place the glass in the transparency holder with the scale on the lens side of the glass. Mask off the area around the glass plate so that the light comes through the 8″ x 10″ areas only.

Place another 8″ x 10″ clear glass plate in the plate holder bars of the camera back. Tape the other half of gray scale B onto the center of this plate.

Now place an 8″x10″ ground glass against this plate and gray scale B.

Focus the image of gray scale A that is being projected by the lens to the same size and alongside gray scale B.

After focusing, close the lens shutter, tip the top of the ground glass back and insert a piece of lith-type film against gray scale B. Bring the top of the ground glass back to hold the film in close contact with the scale.

Expose and develop in a continuous-tone developer, similar to DK50 diluted 1:1, for about two minutes.

Adjust the exposure so that the 2.0 step which was marked on scale A in the transparency holder will have a density above .4 on the negative.

The negative obtained from this test records two gray scales, one made by projection from scale A in the transparency holder, the other made by contact from scale B in the camera back. Plotting the densities of the projected and contact images against the density of the original gives you a simple means of judging the lens flare.

A significant way of expressing lens performance numerically is to give the percent of effective density range delivered by the lens compared to the density range of the copy. Using a standard test density range of 2.0, we simply divide

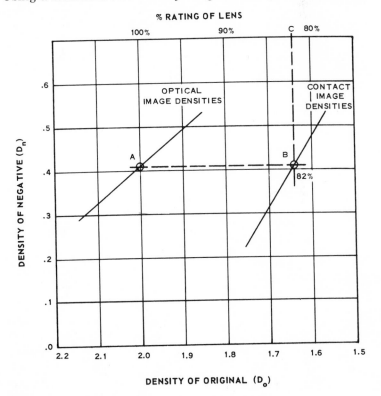

Figure 55   Calculating Percent Lens Flare

this into the actual effective density range of the lens image. A 100 percent lens would deliver an image of 2.0. An image range of 1.80 would come from a 90 percent lens, and 1.6(from an 80 percent lens. Using this rating system, a good lens delivers a 90 percent or better image and a badly scratched lens can deliver as low as 55 percent of the density of the original.

To determine the percentage rating of the lens, the following procedure is used. In Figure 55, the curve drawn for the projected gray scale crosses the 2.0 density point at A. Draw a line from point A, parallel to the horizontal axis (density of original axis), to the curve drawn for the contact gray scale negative. They intersect at point B. From point B draw a perpendicular line to the top of the graph, which has been calibrated in percent. Point C is then the percentage rating of the lens.

Chapter XV

FILTERS

A filter is a colored, transparent medium that permits certain wavelengths or colors of light of the visible spectrum to pass through it. At the same time it blocks the passage of other colors or portions of the spectrum. For lithographic work, these filters are ordinarily made in three ways. The filter may consist of a stained, colored acetate sheet, a stained piece of optical glass, or a gelatin filter made by dyeing a thin sheet of gelatin. The dry gelatin film may then be cemented and bound between pieces of optical glass. In general, we use the gelatin film filter alone.

The gelatin filters in current use are known as Wratten filters. The name is that of the firm that first marketed them. These filters are distinguished by numerical designations. A complete list of the wavelengths transmitted, and the percentage of light transmitted at these wavelengths, is available in published form.[1]

In halftone photography, filters are used most when a colored original is reproduced as a monochrome. In specialized types of line work like the reproduction of a map, for example, the copy may consist of both red and black lines. The requirements may be that the black lines are to be held while the red areas are to be dropped out. In this case, the red area must be photographed as if it were a white area. One way to do this is to use a film material which is sensitive to red. Another method calls for the proper combination of film and filter that will record the red areas as white when the film is exposed. In this particular case, a panchromatic film and a red or an orange filter must be used.

(1) *Wratten Filters,* Eastman Kodak Company, Rochester, New York.

Table VI

FILTER CHART FOR COLOUR CONTRAST PHOTOGRAPHY

COLOUR TO PHOTOGRAPH	SENSITIVITY OF MATERIAL	COLOUR OF FILTER
Red as black	Panchromatic	Green
Red as black	Orthochromatic	Green
Red as black	Colour blind	None
Red as white	Panchromatic	Red or orange
Orange as black	Panchromatic	Green or blue
Orange as black	Orthochromatic	Green or blue
Orange as black	Colour blind	None
Orange as white	Panchromatic	Red or orange
Yellow as black	Panchromatic	Blue
Yellow as black	Orthochromatic	Blue
Yellow as black	Colour blind	None or blue
Yellow as white	Panchromatic	Red or orange
Yellow as white	Orthochromatic	Yellow or orange
Yellow-green as black	Panchromatic	Blue
Yellow-green as black	Orthochromatic	Blue
Yellow-green as black	Colour blind	None or blue
Yellow-green as white	Panchromatic	Green
Yellow-green as white	Orthochromatic	Green or yellow
Green as black	Panchromatic	Red
Green as white	Panchromatic	Green
Green as white	Orthochromatic	Green or yellow
Blue-green as black	Panchromatic	Red
Blue-green as white	Panchromatic	Blue or green
Blue-green as white	Orthochromatic	Blue or green
Blue as black	Panchromatic	Red or orange
Blue as black	Orthochromatic	Yellow or orange
Blue as white	Panchromatic	Blue
Blue as white	Orthochromatic	Blue
Blue as white	Colour blind	None or blue
Violet as black	Panchromatic	Green
Violet as black	Orthochromatic	Deep yellow
Violet as white	Panchromatic	Blue
Violet as white	Orthochromatic	Blue
Violet as white	Colour blind	None or blue

For the reproduction of various colors as either black or white, Table VI indicates which filters to use. It covers most of the situations that are encountered by the average half-tone photographer.

58. FILTER FACTORS

When a filter is used, there are several points that must be considered. One is the amount of exposure increase required. This is known as the *filter factor*. This factor is the amount by which the normal exposure must be multiplied to compensate for the amount of light absorbed by the filter material. This factor depends on the following three items:

1. The type of light source employed.
2. The absorption and transmission characteristics of the filter.
3. The sensitivity of the film material being used.

Light sources vary considerably and this is one point which must be considered when using filters. Some light sources are high in yellow content. Others are low in yellow and high in blue content. If the color of the light source contains a high percentage of yellow, then a yellow filter will allow a large percentage of this light to pass through it. However, with the same light source, a blue filter will not pass very much of the light. This means that the exposure time must be greatly increased to record the image. In other words, if the filter transmits the color of the light that the source is radiating, then a minimum exposure will be required. If, however, the filter absorbs the majority of the radiated light, then the exposure must be greatly increased. The light sensitivity of the film material must also be considered when using filters. Color-blind film is basically sensitive to blue light. Therefore, light that passes through a blue filter will be almost completely recorded on this film. At the same time, yellow light will hardly record on this emulsion even though a filter is not being used. The color sensitivity of a blue-sensitive emulsion is such that it acts as if a yellow filter were in front of the film emulsion.

Suppose we put some numerical values to this problem and see what happens. Assume that we have an orthochromatic film that is 60 percent sensitive to blue light and about 40 percent sensitive to green light. Using a yellow filter which blocks out the blue light with this film means that only 40 percent of the light that passes through the filter is recorded upon the emulsion. Thus, the exposure must be increased about 2 1/2 times that which would be necessary if no filter were used.

A panchromatic film has a different color sensitivity. Approximately two-thirds or 67 percent of its sensitivity is in the blue region of the spectrum. The remaining thirty-three percent is in the red and green regions. When light goes through a yellow filter, the sixty-seven percent of blue light is absorbed and only thirty-three percent of the total light is used to record the image. This means that the exposure has to be increased about three times to compensate for the amount of light that is absorbed by the filter.

DETERMINING THE FILTER FACTOR. It is necessary that the photographer be able to determine the filter factor for the filters that he has to use in his operation. This is true even though the manufacturer of the sensitive material supplies a *relative* filter factor in the data sheet packed with the material. The manufacturer's filter factors are not usually accurate in any given plant due to the variations in the light sources used in different plants. In addition, there are other factors such as development techniques and the type of filter being used (i.e., gelatin, gelatin in optical glass, or optically dyed glass). Sometimes it is necessary for the photographer to use filters other than the ones for which the manufacturer supplies filter factors.

Here is a practical method to determine correct filter factors:

Place a photographic gray scale on the copyboard of the camera. Focus it to any convenient size. Now make a series of adjacent exposures on one piece of film, each exposure for a different time. These exposures can be either continuous-tone or halftone. No filter is used for these exposures. Develop this piece of film for the recommended time suggested by the manufacturer of the material. After it is washed, fixed, and dried, find the particular gray scale which reproduced the best range of tone values. If, for example, you gave a series of exposures of 5, 10, 20, and 40 seconds on a piece of film, the 10-second exposure might have been the one which produced a scale with the best tonal rendition. This scale, then, would be your standard.

Now, using exactly the same set-up, make a series of exposures on another piece of film. In this case, put into the lens the filter whose factor you wish to find. The shortest exposure in the series should not be less than the standard already established, in this case 10 seconds. When processed in the same manner as the original strip, one gray scale exposure will produce an image that is equal in value to that of the 10-second scale previously made. Suppose the exposure for the scale that matched the original standard was 60 seconds. Then, as it took 6 times the exposure with the filter to produce a gray scale with the identical standards, the exposure factor for the filter being tested would be 6. Using this method, additional tests can be made for the other filters that you wish to use, and the filter factors that will be correct in *your* shop under *your* own set of operating conditions will be established.

59. FILTERS AND LIGHT

Filters are colored mediums that either allow the passage of certain wavelengths of light or block them. To clearly understand their action, it is necessary to go a little further in our discussions of light itself.

Light is a form of radiant energy. This means that it is a type of energy that radiates from a source. This energy travels with a wave motion. The effects that are produced depend upon the amplitude or intensity of the wave that is radiated and upon the particular wavelength that is radiated. Both of these factors are functions of the wave characteristic of the particular form of radiant energy.

WAVE LENGTH (λ)
(DISTANCE BETWEEN PEAKS OF TWO WAVES)

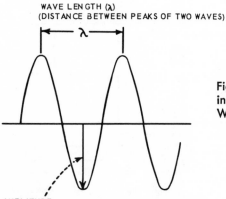

λ

Figure 56 Diagram Illustrating the Properties of Light Waves

AMPLITUDE
(SHOWN BY MAXIMUM DISPLACEMENT OF WAVE)

The wavelength of light is measured from the same point on two successive waves such as the distance between the crests or peaks of two waves. This length is exceedingly small. It is on the order of a one-thousand-millionth part of a meter, and the common term for this fraction is "milli-micron." This is abbreviated m*u* and is the standard term used in measuring such items as the color sensitivity of an emulsion. Another term that is used is "Angstrom" units (Å). The Angstrom unit is equal to one-tenth of a millimicron.

The visible spectrum is included in the wavelength range of from approximately 400 m*u* to 700 m*u*. Within this range, the portion from 400 m*u* to 500 m*u* is mostly blue in color, the portion from 500 m*u* to 600 m*u* is mostly green in color, and the portion from 600 m*u* to 700 m*u* is mostly red. Ultra-violet light is below 400 m*u*, infrared above 700 m*u*. The films that we use in the lithographic industry have their color sensitivity in the following ranges of wavelengths:

Color-blind emulsions............400 m*u*-540 m*u*
Orthochromatic emulsions.........400 m*u*-600 m*u*
Panchromatic emulsions...........400 m*u*-700 m*u*

Figure 57 compares the range covered by the human eye with the wavelength ranges of various photographic emulsions:

Photographic light sources used in lithographic work, generate several ranges of wavelengths of light rather than a single one. This grouping of wavelengths is known as a spec-

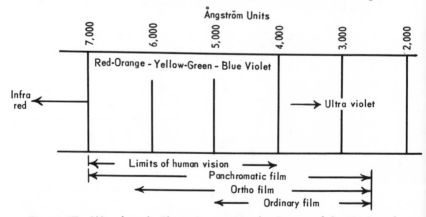

Figure 57   Wavelength Chart Comparing the Range of Sensitivity of the Human Eye With Various Types of Film Emulsions

trum. The materials that are used to construct our filters pass or block bands of wavelengths of light in the spectrum. Some of the wavelengths pass, some of the others block, and still others are transmitted with only a change in amplitude (intensity).

This blocking of some of the wavelengths of light that might otherwise pass through a filter is known as the selective absorption of the filter. It means that the filter is composed of such a material that it will be selective in its absorption of some of the wavelengths of light that we attempt to transmit through it. We can look at this picture of filter action from the other side by saying that a filter has the property of selective transmission. By this we mean that the material comprising a filter will transmit certain wavelengths of the light that strikes its surface. Generally speaking, filters transmit light of their own color and block all other colors.

From the description of the processes of selective absorption and transmission, it would seem logical that a given filter would be more or less effective in certain portions of the spectrum than in others. In the areas of the spectrum where the filter is effective, a great majority of the light that falls upon the filter is absorbed. However, in moving from one wavelength to another, the filter does not pass or block

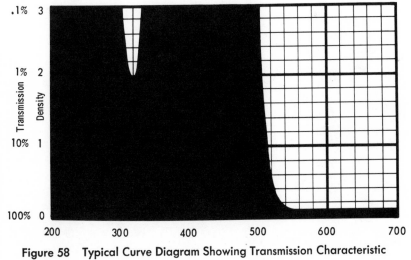

Figure 58 Typical Curve Diagram Showing Transmission Characteristic of a Filter

abruptly. There is no single wavelength that is transmitted 100 percent with the very next wavelength being absorbed 100 percent. Rather, there is a gradual blending from high transmission through a falling scale to lesser transmission. This is contrary to the common belief that a filter only permits full transmission of a few selected wavelengths and fully absorbs all the other wavelengths.

The actual transmission and absorption of a filter can be found in diagrams such as that in Figure 58. It shows both the wavelengths transmitted and the percentage of the incident light transmitted at a given wavelength.

Chapter XVI

SPECIAL HALFTONE CAMERA TECHNIQUES

In every class of photographic work there are special techniques unique to the particular method that is being used. This is true in halftone photography as it is in all other phases of photography. This chapter discusses some special halftone camera techniques that are used. The techniques that are discussed are the ones that the average halftone photographer should know for his day-to-day work. It is true that he will not have to use these every day, but rarely will a period of time go by during which one or more of the techniques is not required or asked for.

60. SCREEN TINTS

The halftone photographer is usually called upon to produce screen tints that are to be used by the stripping department within a plant. With these tints, the stripper is able to lay in a flat tone of a given strength over a desired area. This flat tint must be more even in tone value over a larger area than a camera tint shot from artwork. Unless this tint is even, it will create an annoying visual impression.

The difficulty for the halftone photographer is that although the production of screen tints seems relatively simple, the production of *even* screen tints is difficult. There are a few factors over which the photographer has no control, such as the evenness of the emulsion coating. However, even if this were perfect, the usual techniques used by the photographer would leave much to be desired. So, to study the problem of producing even screen tints, we will concentrate mostly on the controls that the photographer can establish, and the changes he can make in his normal working routine to produce better and more even screen tints.

As a standard of comparison, let us describe a typical procedure that is used for the production of a screen tint. The photographer will usually set up his camera at same-size and place a large sheet of white paper (such as a cast-coated sheet) in his copyboard. After illuminating the white paper as evenly as possible, he will move his screen into position and make the exposure. Usually a great deal of care will be taken in the development of the negative in an effort to get an even image. The photographer may resort to still-development to help obtain this even image. Finally, the processed negative will be dried, and the screen tint is finished.

A few of the variations that the photographer might use to get a better result are the following:

1. A flash lamp for the light source rather than white paper on the copyboard.

2. Very small apertures.

3. Removing the lens and placing a round aperture where the lens would normally be.

4. Brush development for smoother results.

5. Diffusion of the light source.

Certain faults are common with the average screen tint made in the camera. The two most important are: 1) The dot size is uneven. Usually, the dot in the center of the tint will be a different strength than the dot toward the edge of the tint. This means that within a 20″ x 24″ image area, only an area about 8″ x 10″ in the center would have dots of equal size; 2) The image is streaky. This fault creates blotchy areas throughout the entire image. In the majority of cases, this is due to faulty development. However, this is not the only reason.

Let us look, then, at the materials, equipment, and methods used in the production of a screen tint, and see where problems arise and how they might be solved.

60A. Light Sources for Screen Tints. Our first factor is the light source. Ordinarily it is one of two types: 1) Arc light reflected from a copy of equal brightness; 2) A flash lamp shining directly into the lens. Arc lamps are a faulty light source because they flicker and cause an uneven amount of illumination to be radiated to the copy and thence reflected to the lens. In addition, changes in the voltage or current when lamps are in series may cause a difference in illumination from each lamp. Another reason for arc lamps being faulty was suggested by Bruno and Atkinson[1]. They state:

"... Arc lights give off a high percentage of ultraviolet radiation. Generally this is beneficial in photography because it reduces exposure times; but when the photography involves a glass screen, it causes serious complications. Glass screens are cemented with canada balsam which is fluorescent ... it absorbs ultraviolet radiation and transforms it into visible light. Since the glass used in screen manufacture is not optically flat when two surfaces are cemented together, the canada balsam between them varies in thickness. Thus, the amount of ultraviolet absorbed and transmitted by different areas over the screen varies and causes corresponding variations on the emulsion. This fact is seldom considered in halftone photography, yet it is one of the most significant causes of irregularities and unevenness in screen tints."

Flash lamps, on the other hand, contain an incandescent light source which is considerably more stable than light from an arc. And, as stability of illumination is one of the prime factors in a light source, the incandescent light has the advantage. In addition, further stabilization of light by the use of voltage regulators or other means is considerably less expensive with incandescent lamps than with arc lamps. All of these reasons, therefore, favor the incandescent lamp over the arc light as a light source for making screen tints.

60B. Lens Flare and Screen Tints. Our second problem area is concerned with the process lens. With an uncoated lens, the problem of lens flare is brought into the picture. Here, the internal reflections within the lens add the equivalent of a fogging exposure to certain areas of the image. This can be an important and often unsuspected source of uneven illumination.

60C. Vignetting. Another factor is the aperture head. When large apertures are used, the light rays from the extremes of the copy are cut off due to "vignetting." This, however, can be eliminated to a great extent by stopping down the lens.

60D. Light Variation With Angular Distance. The final factor to consider in the production of good screen tints is the fact

(1) M. H. Bruno and F. A. Atkinson, "The Production of Even Screen Tints," *Modern Lithography,* March 1946, page 51.

that the illumination striking the emulsion will vary depending upon its angular distance from the axis of the lens. Light reflected from the edge of the copy, and traveling diagonally through the lens to the edge of the film, travels a greater distance than light from the center of the copy. Even the light entering the lens from a flash lamp will still vary depending upon the angle at which it emerges from the lens. If we consider the light traveling along the optical axis as 100 percent illumination, then the relative intensities of the light striking at different angles will be approximately that shown in Figure 59.

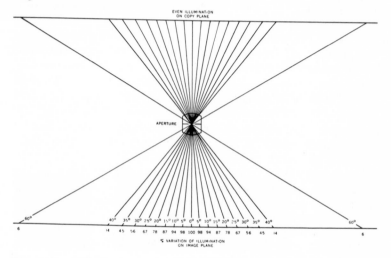

Figure 59   Fall-off of Light at Various Angles of Incidence

60E. Development Factors. The problems inherent in development result in major faults when trying to make good screen tints. When negatives are developed in trays, it is difficult to produce a method of agitation that is even over the entire surface of the negative being developed. Swirling the solution or rocking it usually creates a faster development along the walls of the tray where the solution is more rapidly agitated.

Although still-development is better, it offers no guarantee to the problem of development streaks and hot spots. One answer that is promising, however, is the use of the new nitrogen burst development equipment. Experiments with this system have shown promise as an exceptionally uniform method of development.

60F. Suggestions for Better Screen Tints. To eliminate the various faults that we have discussed, Bruno and Atkinson[1] have suggested a method that is basically sound. This method with certain variations can produce excellent tints. Let us, then, discuss some of the steps that were suggested.

1. *The lens is replaced by a stop.* This removes the problems of lens flare and vignetting and, as the halftone screen projects an image of the opening used, a stop is just as satisfactory as a lens. Waterhouse stops work well. Or, stops can be made by cutting holes in thin black films or thin metal strips. In any event, the hole must be cut cleanly without ragged edges. To vary the pattern produced, the stop can be varied. A straight-line stop will produce a straight-line tint, etc. Figure 60 shows this relationship between the stop used and the tint produced.

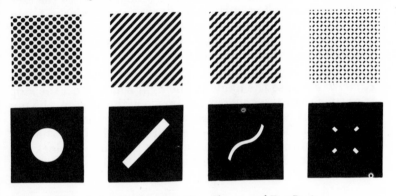

Figure 60   Relationship Between Stop Shape and Tint Design

2. *A long bellows extension is used.* By using a maximum bellows extension rather than same-size extension, the angle of field can be considerably reduced. In the test case, with a bellows extension of 72 inches on a 24 x 24 inch U. S. Army camera, the angle of field on a 20 x 24 inch image area was reduced to about 12 degrees. This is the equivalent of a loss of only 8 percent of the illumination at the edges.

3. *A tungsten light source and double diffuser are used instead of white paper and arc light.* The tungsten source eliminates the problems created by arc lamps. The specially-made unit consisted of four 100-watt frosted bulbs mounted

(1) M. H. Bruno and F. A. Atkinson, "The Production of Even Screen Tints," *Modern Lithography,* March 1946, page 51.

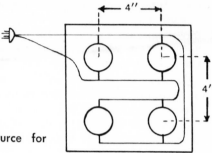

Figure 61 Special Light Source for Production of Even Tints

on a plywood base and centered in the corners of a four-inch square. They were wired in parallel. For accurate alignment the center of the light unit, the center of the stop, and the center of the screen must all lie on a straight line. In the case of the 72-inch bellows extension, Bruno and Atkinson found that the optimum position was with the end of the bulbs at 15 inches from the stop. The diffuser consists of two sheets of grained acetate to cover the stop.

4. *Blinds are used to cut out stray reflections within the camera.* Because the angle of the light source with the stop is greater than the angle of the image with the stop, the unwanted light entering the lens would be internally reflected within the bellows. If light blinds are placed within the bellows in front of the screen, they can be made to block the rays reflected from the internal sides of the camera. These

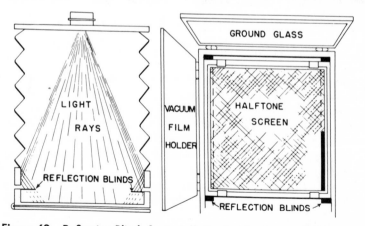

Figure 62   Reflection Blinds for Installation Inside Camera Bellows

blinds can be made of black-lined cardboard such as that used for film boxes.

The only additional factor suggested by Bruno and Atkinson was that they used a set screen distance (14/64 of an inch) and varied the size of the stop opening to obtain the various size dot tints. A 1/2-inch stop was used for pinpoints to 30 percent dots. A 1-inch stop covered from 20 percent to 75 percent dots, and a 1 7/16-inch stop produced dots from 60 percent to 90 percent. Examples of the dot sizes produced with the various size stops are shown in Figure 63.

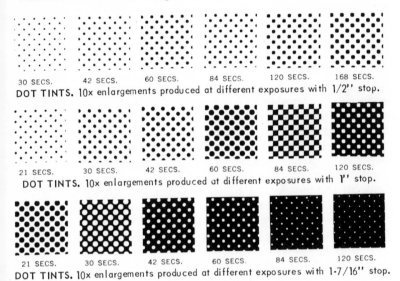

| 30 SECS. | 42 SECS. | 60 SECS. | 84 SECS. | 120 SECS. | 168 SECS. |

DOT TINTS. 10x enlargements produced at different exposures with 1/2'' stop.

| 21 SECS. | 30 SECS. | 42 SECS. | 60 SECS. | 84 SECS. | 120 SECS. |

DOT TINTS. 10x enlargements produced at different exposures with 1'' stop.

| 21 SECS. | 30 SECS. | 42 SECS. | 60 SECS. | 84 SECS. | 120 SECS. |

DOT TINTS. 10x enlargements produced at different exposures with 1-7/16'' stop.

Figure 63   Relationship Between Size of Stop and Dot Size in Even Tints

Additional hints for the processing operation were:

1. Have plenty of developer in the tray — no less than 1 inch deep, usually between 1-1 1/2 inches.

2. Cover the negative evenly and completely with developer.

3. Rinse the negative thoroughly in water before you put it in the hypo bath.

These are the recommendations suggested by Bruno and Atkinson for the production of even screen tints and which produce very acceptable tints. However, here are some additional suggestions on the production of even screen tints:

1. The reflection blinds used within the camera are most important to success in producing even screen tints. They can be left in the camera for normal operation and will prove valuable.

2. Development is an extremely critical factor. With the usual tray method of development the developer at the edges of the negative receives more agitation and develops the edges of the negative more than the central area. The still-development technique offers some improvement over normal agitation. (With still-development, you agitate for approximately one minute, and then allow the negative to remain still in the quiet developer for the remainder of the development period.) However, even still-development may not give the results desired.

One of the best manual development techniques employs a four-inch camel's hair brush, swabbed evenly over the entire surface of the emulsion, first in vertical and then in horizontal strokes. The smoothness that results from this development technique is apparent almost from the very first attempt.

If the plant work requires the production of many tint negatives, nitrogen burst developing equipment may be a good investment. This equipment consists of a stainless steel tank for the developing solution. It is equipped with a water jacket to keep the temperature of the developer constant. A grid of plastic tubing about 1/4 inch in diameter is installed in the bottom of the tank. The tubing has tiny holes drilled in it throughout its length. One end of the tubing is sealed. The other end is connected to a fitting that extends through the walls of the tank and the water jacket. On the outside and connected to the fitting, more tubing leads to a clock-controlled valve and from here to a tank of nitrogen gas.

The films to be developed are placed in stainless steel racks and hung in the developing solution. During development, the nitrogen gas is released into the plastic grid in the bottom of the tank, where it bubbles upward agitating the solution. Two timers are used. One controls the duration of the individual bursts of the gas and the other controls the time between the bursts. Nitrogen is used because it is inert and does not affect the chemical reaction of the developing solution on the exposed film.

Such equipment does an excellent job and eliminates the inherent disadvantages of manual tray development. Tests at the LTF laboratory have shown that best results are obtained with equipment designed for the next size larger film than is ordinarily used. In other words, if most of your work is with 8 x 10-inch film, use equipment that will accept 11 x 14-inch film.

3. The use of a constant voltage regulator in the electrical circuit ahead of the 100-watt bulbs will eliminate some of the fluctuations in the intensity of the illumination.

4. If film is used for the sensitive material, tape it to a glass support before you develop it. This is especially important when brush development is to be used.

5. Developer temperature must be kept accurate to within one-half of one degree.

6. Use a minimum amount of developer, especially with brush development. Use fresh developer for each film or plate developed.

Throughout this whole section, we have been discussing the production of a so-called "master" tint. From tints produced by this technique, and to this standard of quality, additional positive or negative tints can be made by contact. Although there are still restrictions on what can be done to produce an even print — even with contacts — they are nowhere near as stringent as for the master tints we are discussing. With contact tints, the two primary factors are evenness of the light source and care in development.

A good developer for use in making these screen tints is the following:

CRAMER PROCESS DEVELOPER

	Metric Units	U. S. Units
Solution A:		
Water (warm)	1 liter	32 liq. oz.
Hydroquinone	45 grams	1 1/2 av. oz.
Sodium Sulfite	30 grams	1 av. oz.
Sulfuric Acid, C.P.	4 cc.	1/8 liq. oz.
Solution B:		
Water (warm)	1 liter	32 liq. oz.
Sodium Carbonate	30 grams	1 av. oz.
Potassium Carbonate	90 grams	3 av. oz.
Sodium Sulfite	90 grams	3 av. oz.
Potassium Bromide	8 grams	120 grains

To use: Mix equal parts of A and B. Develop for 5 minutes at 68° F.

61. DROPOUT NEGATIVES (HIGHLIGHT NEGATIVES)

The varieties of artwork that are presented to the half-tone photographer in the course of production very often include an art or photographic subject that calls for a completely white background or area. In many cases the detail is so complex that the time necessary for hand correction of these areas by etching or opaquing becomes impractical. When this problem is faced, one answer is the production of a dropout negative. This type of negative creates enough density in the highlight areas so that all detail is removed and no dot prints in the immediate highlight areas. Another method occasionally employed to produce a dropout negative is by highlight masking. Let us discuss these methods in a bit more detail.

61A. Large Aperture Exposures. This is one of the simplest methods of dropping out a white area. A portion of the exposure given with a glass screen to produce the required range of tones is made through an aperture that is much larger than normal. An f16 or f11 aperture is commonly used. This exposure is relatively short, usually for only a few seconds. This added amount of exposure will not distort the tone reproduction abnormally, but it will be enough to close up the small openings in the highlight area.

61B. Supplementary Line Exposure. In this procedure, the half-tone exposure is made, and the screen is removed. A screen compensating glass is dropped into position, and a short line exposure is made. This exposure would be about 1/25 of the exposure given for the halftone, if the same aperture were to be used. The line exposure creates a slight fogging action which is sufficient to close up the small dots in the highlight areas. If too much line exposure is given, the fogging action will carry into the middletone areas causing a loss of detail. If short-developed, the shadows will run together.

61C. Sears Method.[1] This method approaches the dropout problem from a slightly different point of view. It requires a continuous-tone negative and produces a final screened positive. Mr. Sears proposes that you first shoot a heavy, contrasty, continuous-tone negative. This negative would have a density range of approximately 1.50. The highlights could have a density of about 2.00 and the shadows a density of

---

(1) F. W. Sears, British Patent #10,855, 1904.

about 0.50. The negative is then placed in the transparency holder, and a halftone positive is made without any flash exposure. The dense portions of the negative are such that the positive can be shot without getting a dot in the highlight area. If a final negative is desired, it can be produced by contact from the positive. One advantage of this method is that it permits some hand correction on the continuous-tone negative or halftone positive if necessary.

61D. Overlay Mask Method. A second negative is made in addition to the halftone negative when using this procedure. This new negative is continuous-tone, very light in density, and contrasty. It is shot at the same time as the halftone negative. If a glass screen was used for the halftone exposure, remove it and put the screen compensating glass into position. The weak negative is then shot. This negative will usually have a maximum density of about 0.30 to 0.50. Tape it in register over the halftone negative. The exposure on the plate, or on another film to make a positive halftone image, is made through the two negatives. The added density of the weak continuous-tone image is sufficient to hold back the light in the highlight areas so that no dot will print.

61E. Other Methods. At various times in the past, additional methods for securing dropout negatives have been suggested. O. Mente, in 1905, suggested that a negative of this type might be made by using a square diaphragm with its sides parallel to the lines of the halftone screen. L. Bassani (1923)[1] suggested a special mechanism which would allow the screen to be rotated while being held in the same plane. After the main exposure is made, the screen is moved a carefully calculated distance, and then is rotated in a small circular movement. A similar effect can be obtained by rotating a diaphragm in the same way, and this method has also been proposed. An additional method of utilizing screen movement has been proposed by B. E. Tory in his recent volume.[2]

Most of the additional methods proposed have the fault, for the average busy photographer, of requiring special equipment or additional steps that take too much time from usual production schedules. For this reason, it will be found that the two most generally satisfactory methods are those using

(1) L. Bassani, French Patents 586,101 (1923); 602,692 (1924).
(2) B. E. Tory, *Photolithography*, Associated General Publications Pty. Ltd., Sydney, Australia, 1953.

the large aperture or the supplementary line exposure. Both are easily adapted to regular routine, and the time involved in their use is negligible.

62. RE-SCREENING HALFTONES

Re-screening a halftone means that a halftone image is the copy, and is re-photographed through a halftone screen to produce a new halftone negative or positive. A typical case is as follows: A large manufacturer is having a book printed describing his products. On one of the pages he decided to re-produce, in a very small size, the magazine ads that he has used in his advertising campaign during the past year. You, as photographer, are given proof sheets of these color ads and told to reduce them to fit the layout. Although the origi-nals are four-color ads, the reproduction in the new book are to be black-and-white halftones, and you are to re-screen the larger halftone color proofs.

If the copy were a line shot or a continuous-tone original, there would be little or no problem. However, when you must re-screen a halftone original, you face the problem of moiré.

Moiré is a type of pattern that is formed when two or more screen images are overlapped with almost identical angles. The patterns that are formed vary in type but are usually geometrical. The smaller the angular difference be-tween the two halftone images, the greater the spread of the pattern within an area. As the angular distance increases, the pattern opens up, and at an angle of approximately 30 de-grees seems to disappear entirely.

What actually forms this moiré pattern is dots of both screened images coinciding in an area. Gradually they sep-arate, overlap, and finally coincide again. This process, re-peating itself over and over again, forms the enlarged pattern over the entire screened area.

When re-screening halftones, the simplest way to eliminate the moiré pattern is to rotate the screen or copy until the point is reached where the moiré pattern on the ground glass disappears or is least objectionable. With a circular glass screen, the image can be inspected on the ground glass while the screen is being rotated until the proper angle is reached. With a rectanuglar screen, the copy is rotated, preferably by someone else, while the photographer is watching the change in the pattern on the ground glass.

The moiré pattern becomes more pronounced as colors become darker. Therefore, when re-screening color halftones, the best arrangement is to try to eliminate the moiré pattern with the original color that is strongest. This is usually the black. In this way the least objectionable secondary effects will occur.

When re-screening a halftone image that has black in it, the most probable angle of the black image is 45 degrees. Therefore, if this is the condition, then by rotating the screen or copy 30 degrees, the moiré will usually be completely eliminated. This means that the screen will be at either 15 or 75 degrees, if it is the screen that is rotated.

63. DUOTONES

This is one topic that cannot be discussed until a definition is offered. In the author's experience, the following half dozen kinds of copy have been supplied and referred to as a duotone:

1. A black or dark-colored halftone image printed over a lighter solid-color background.

2. A black or dark-colored halftone image printed over a colored tint background.

3. A black or dark-colored halftone printed over a color tint background with various areas eliminated from the tint background by hand.

4. A black or dark-colored halftone printed over a lighter solid color with areas of both the tint and the halftone removed by hand.

5. A black or dark-colored halftone printed over a lighter colored halftone where both picture areas are different.

6. An illustration where portions are in black or dark-colored halftone, and other portions are reproduced as a lighter colored line photograph.

Naturally, from even this partial list of the types of copy supplied, you will get the idea that the only thing they seem to have in common is that the final image consists of two colors.

There are many conflicting ideas as to what constitutes a duotone, not only in the lithographic industry, but also in the advertising field and other related industries. As an attempt at more orderly thinking, the following definition is offered:

"A duotone is a two-color halftone image made from a single piece of continuous-tone, black-and-white copy with both printed images recording the approximate tonal relations of the original. The image printed with the darkest color emphasizes the shadow end of the illustration, while the image printed with the lightest color emphasizes the highlight end."

A duotone is made from *a single piece of copy.* It is continuous-tone and can be either a photograph or artwork. This copy is photographed twice through a halftone screen. Each image is recorded at a different angle and on a different piece of film. When shot, the tonal scale of one of the images is changed slightly to create a more pleasing effect. Finally, the two images are printed in register on the press. One of the images — the dominant one — is usually printed in a dark color and the other image is printed in a light color.

63A. Preparing the Copy for a Duotone. When copy is received to make a duotone, the photographer should first place register marks around the image area. This is to facilitate the registering of the final images. In addition, a continuous-tone gray scale should be placed next to the copy to evaluate more accurately the tonal values on the two negatives that are to be produced. At this time, the photographer should find out what color is to be printed for the second color as this will determine to some extent the tonal range of negative that is to be shot for the second color.

63B. Shooting the Primary Negative. The primary negative is the one that will be printed in the darker color. This is most often black. The halftone screen is set to shoot this image at an angle of 45 degrees. The negative is shot in the same manner as a normal halftone negative with one exception. The shadow dot is made a little larger than usual. The shot is made so that the printed result will be a dot of approximately 85 percent in this area. This is done so that when the second color is printed over this shadow area it will not be too closed in and allow some secondary color to show in the shadow detail.

63C. Shooting the Secondary Negative. The secondary negative is the one that will be printed in the lighter color. The tonal range of this negative is also made differently than a full-range halftone negative. It is shot so that there will be little or no dot in the shadow area of the negative, but will print an approximate 25 percent dot in the highlights. This allows the color image to come up in the highlight area and create a more pleasing effect. The secondary negative is usually shot at a 30 degree angular difference from the primary negative to eliminate any possible moiré effects. This means that the negative is shot at either 15 or 75 degrees. Either one of these screen angles will produce satisfactory results. In the event that a circular screen is not available, it will be necessary to place the copy on the copyboard at an angle.

63D. Variations on a Theme. The previous description of a duotone was, by the definition given, a true duotone. There are, as previously mentioned, various other combinations of images that are called duotones. Probably the most common of these is the use of a black halftone image printed on a color tint. In this case, the tint is laid in by a stripper rather than having the photographer do any work other than perhaps shooting the tint. In most cases a tint value of about 50 percent or lighter is chosen, and the photographer shoots his negative for a normal tonal value. In other words, he does not attempt to keep the shadow area opened as he did on the normal duotone. The screen tint is set in by the stripper at the correct angle.

A common variation of the overall tint method described above is the use of a tint color in background areas only. In this case the halftone is made and the tint is laid in by the stripper. However, prior to the plates being made, the tint is blocked out in the main areas of the image. In this manner the main halftone image is printed in black, and the color is printed as a flat tint in the background areas only, being removed from the main areas of the image.

Still another method has been suggested. A single halftone negative is made in the camera rather than the two negatives that are usually made for a duotone. From this negative, two contact positives are produced to make the duotone. The positive that is to print in the darker color is exposed normally. However, the positive that is being made to print in the lighter color of the duotone is deliberately overexposed to enlarge the dots. This exposure would have to be in the order of from two to six times the normal exposure. Although you might think that this procedure would create a moiré pattern, apparently it does not and is said to work very well.

64. OPAQUING MASKS

The necessity of dropping out the whites exists in the reproduction of many pieces of artwork. One approach to this problem has been covered in the section on dropout negatives. However, the dropout negative will distort the highlight tones in the original and the art may have important detail in this area that must be carried in the final print. When this is the case, the production of an opaquing mask is a valuable aid. It enables the photographer to drop out the white areas, and at the same time hold the important tones that are in the highlight area. In effect, it eliminates hand-opaquing the negatives at these points, and this gives the technique its name.

The opaquing mask is a high-contrast negative that records only the whites and the very near whites in the original. It is made on a lith-type emulsion and developed in the standard developer. Its exposure and development times vary considerably from a normal line shot, although this is basically a line negative.

The camera is first set to shoot the halftone of the original art. Then the screen is removed and the camera is prepared for a same-size line shot. In the event a glass screen is used, the screen compensating glass is put into position behind the lens. On lith-type film, an exposure is made that is approximately one-sixth to one-quarter of your standard line exposure time through whatever aperture you ordinarily use. Develop the negative in the standard developer for the particular film being used. The development is done by inspection, and is not carried to completion (2 1/4 minutes with most emulsions). The development is continued only until the white areas come up to the point where they are just starting to turn black. Depending upon the method of handling, this can take anywhere from 1 1/2 to 4 minutes. Use a gray scale alongside the copy for control of highlight density.

Even though the white areas recorded on this negative are not totally black, they afford sufficient density to fog the white areas on subsequent exposures either to contact film or directly to the plate. In the event the negative picks up a pale ghost tint in areas other than those desired, the tint can be easily removed with a short application of Farmer's reducer.

In use, the opaquing mask is registered with the halftone image, and the later exposures are made through the combination of these two films. Because of the necessity of registration between the two images, you must be certain to put register marks on the copy prior to shooting.

65. THE INDIRECT PROCESS OF MAKING HALFTONE IMAGES

The indirect process of making halftone positives consists of shooting a continuous-tone negative, and then shooting a halftone positive from that negative. In the event a halftone negative is needed as the final image before going to the plate, it is made from the halftone positive by contact.

There are several reasons for taking this added step in the procedure. One may be that the original requires a great deal of handwork. The halftone image can withstand only a certain amount of handwork. Usually the variation accomplished on the halftone is to change the halftone dot no more than 25 percent. When a greater change in tone value is required, the halftone dot image will not stand the amount of correction necessary. The continuous-tone image, however, can be varied a much greater amount than the halftone image. Therefore, when considerable work must be done to the image, the indirect process will allow for this greater amount of correction.

Still another reason for the use of the indirect process is that it will allow a fuller tonal gradation and will pick up the more subtle tone variations that are usually lost when an image is shot directly through the halftone screen. By shooting the continuous-tone image of the original to a higher contrast, the tonal range of the copy may be lengthened effectively. This, therefore, allows for more distinction between tones when the halftone positive is made.

When the original is of poor quality, and yet must be reproduced in various sizes, the indirect process offers another advantage. It allows the photographer to make one negative, make the necessary tonal corrections on this negative, and then shoot his various sized copies from this improved continuous-tone negative rather than from the poor original copy.

65A. Procedure for Shooting the Continuous-Tone Negative. The first step in the production of a halftone image by the indirect process is to make a continuous-tone negative of the original. The copy needs no special preparation except that the addition of a continuous-tone gray scale near the picture area will help the photographer considerably in judging the results that he obtains.

The next step is to select the proper type of film to be used to make the continuous-tone negative. If the original is a black-and-white copy, then it can be photographed on either a blue-sensitive or an orthochromatic material. Representative examples of continuous-tone emulsions are Kodak Commercial for the blue-sensitive material, and Kodak Commercial Ortho for the orthochromatic.

If the original is in color, then the film to use would be orthochromatic (in the event that sensitivity to the red portion of the spectrum is not required), or panchromatic (such as Kodak Panatomic-X Sheet Film). It must be understood that although these types of emulsions are representative for the type of work described, they are not always used. For example, on occasion one might shoot color copy on a blue-sensitive emulsion, or black-and-white copy on a panchromatic emulsion.

The selection of a proper developer to be used with the film being shot can be checked by referring to the recommendation of the manufacturer. Perhaps the nearest thing to an all-around developer of excellent characteristics is the DK-50 formula. Rarely do you run across an emulsion for the purpose of indirect halftone photography that cannot be satisfactorily developed in this solution. This particular developer will produce a negative of normal contrast. If greater contrast is required than is obtainable with DK-50, the D-11 formula is an excellent choice.

Although exposure of these materials will vary in every shop, depending upon the conditions, the following is an example of an exposure that is typical:

EMULSION: Kodak Commercial Sheet Film
DEVELOPER: DK-50 (stock solution) at 68° F
LIGHTING: Four 35-ampere arc lamps, two on each side of the copy, 60 inches from the center of the copyboard
APERTURE: f32
MAGNIFICATION: Same-size
EXPOSURE: Eighteen seconds (sixteen Luxometer units)
DEVELOPMENT TIME: Three minutes

DENSITY RANGE:	Original	Negative
Highlight	0.00	1.68
Shadow	1.87	0.32
Range	1.87	1.36

65B. Procedure for Shooting the Halftone Positive. After the negative has been developed, it can be retouched if necessary. Areas can be reduced or intensified and the tone scale distorted in any way necessary to produce the desired final image. When ready, the negative is placed in the positive holder of the camera. The arc lamps are set behind an intervening opal or ground glass diffusing screen so that the light can be transmitted through the negative in order to shoot the halftone positive. The procedure at this point is as follows:

1. Focus the image to the desired size.
2. Prepare your standard lith-type developer.
3. Place screen in position.
4. Expose the film according to your own standards to produce what you believe will be a full-scale reproduction.
5. Process the halftone positive.
6. While still wet, check the positive by looking first at the gray scale. Does it fully record the range of tones that you desire? Do you have a pinpoint dot in the highlights and are your shadows almost a solid? Is there definition between adjoining steps on the gray scale?
7. Now check the copy. Are the tone values what you desire? Are your highlights, middletones, and shadows correct?
8. If your answer to Step 6 or 7 is "no," determine what adjustments are necessary and re-make the positive. Should you change from a one-stop exposure to a two- or three-stop exposure? Do you need more or less exposure?
9. Re-shoot the positive based on the necessary corrections.

This method of producing a halftone image will not be, as you have probably noticed, very much different from your normal method of production. But, if the intermediate continuous-tone negative was of good quality, then the end result — the halftone positive — should have a greater range of tones than the negative, and a smoother transition from one tone to the next. In addition, of course, any correction made on the negative should show up, as desired, on the halftone positive.

65C. Hints for the Indirect Process. Here are a few hints that are suggested to help you over the little rough spots that come along. They may be just the points that are needed to make the good job an excellent one. They are as follows:

1. If reduction is to be done on the continuous-tone negative or the halftone positive, do not use the normal amount

of hardener in your hypo. A lesser amount (approximately 2/3 of normal) will allow the emulsion to be reduced more easily.

2. A change in contrast can be obtained with the halftone screen by changing its distance from the film. Moving the screen in toward the film will lower the contrast, and moving it out toward the lens will increase the contrast. A change of 1/64 of an inch from the correct distance will change the contrast about 10 percent.

66. IMAGE REVERSAL

Within the scope of normal lithographic operations, there are occasions when a reversed image of the copy is desired. It is possible to reverse a plate or film in the camera back, compensate for focus, shoot through the back of the emulsion support, and obtain the desired reversed image. However, the anti-halation backings put on the photo-sensitive materials generally used for lithography can cause streaks and otherwise distort the image. If reversed images make up a good portion of the work load, a mirror or prism device can be purchased. This is attached to the camera lens, and optically reverses the image directly upon the sensitive emulsion. When using such a device, the camera back holding the sensitive emulsion and the copyboard are usually set at right angles to each other, rather than parallel. In one method, the copyboard is constructed so that it lies parallel to the floor and under the lens. Through these devices the image is rotated 90 degrees, and for that reason they are referred to as *right-angle prisms or mirrors.*

In purchasing or using such a device, you must consider the type of reverser (mirror or prism) that will be used. The straight-line reverser allows a lateral reversal of the image through the use of a three-mirror system with the camera components still kept in a straight line. Another straight-line reversing system is incorporated into a recently developed lens — the Goertz Artar Reversing Lens. The lateral reversal of the image is obtained by the use of a prism placed between the front and rear elements of the lens.

MIRRORS AND PRISMS. If a mirror is to be used, it must be a first-surface mirror. This means that the reflecting surface is on its outer face. Common mirrors are second-surface mirrors, where the silver reflecting-coating is on the back sur-

Figure 64 Straight-Line Image Reverser

face. This means that the light rays must pass through the outer surface of the glass, through the glass, and then strike the interior-mirror surface before it is reflected back again through the system. When this is the case, there is a secondary reflection from the front-glass surface that causes distortions and a secondary image.

Although both the mirror and prism have certain faults that prevent them from being perfect instruments, the mirror system is the better of the two for image reversal. Following are some of the advantages and disadvantages of both systems:

1. The mirror absorbs less light than the prism, therefore it will reflect a greater percentage of the light rays that fall upon it.

2. Provided that its size is large enough, the mirror does not limit the angle of view. The prism, however, even with an enlargement of size, will eventually limit the angle of view.

3. With a prism, the angle of view cannot exceed 30 degrees. Beyond this, the rays of light entering the prism will be reflected from the two internal surfaces rather than the single surface of the hypotenuse of the prism itself.

4. The mirror surface is more easily damaged than the prism.

5. Compared to a prism, the large surface of a mirror is more exposed to possible damage from vapors, gases, and ruinous scratches than the smaller surface of a prism.

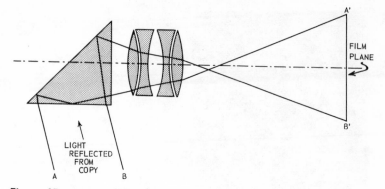

Figure 65   Action of the Prism Image Reverser

6. The reflecting coating on the hypotenuse of the prism is considerably more stable.

7. If the prism is intended for color work, another type of distortion becomes a problem. Rays of white light entering a prism do not follow identical paths within the prism. Thus, while the existing rays leaving the prism will be parallel, they will not coincide into a single sharp image which can be obtained when a mirror is used. The difference in distance between the focal points of the red and blue images may be approximately 1/32 of an inch. To quote from L. P. Clerc: "The difference of focus between the red and the blue images reaches approximately 1/40 of an inch in the case of a prism 4 inches square. Whereas there would be perfect coincidence of the images after reflection from a mirror."[1]

8. With right-angle mirrors and prisms it is necessary that the camera bellows be set at an angle of 90 degrees to the copyboard. However, with the use of a "straight-line" reverser, it is not necessary for this angular set between bellows and copyboard.

---

(1) L. P. Clerc, *Ilford Manual of Process Work,* Third Edition, Ilford Ltd., Ilford, London, 1941, page 12.

Appendix I

DENSITY TABLE

In practical work it is sometimes necessary to find the transmittance or reflectance of a tone area from its density, or to find the density of the tone area from its transmittance or reflectance. The following table can be used in such cases. It gives the values of transmittance or reflectance, expressed in percentages, corresponding to density values ranging from zero to 3.00.

So far as the table is concerned, it makes no difference whether you are working with transmission densities or with reflection densities. If you have a *transmission* density of 1.36, the number opposite 1.36 in the table — 4.365% — is the *transmittance* of the tone area. On the other hand, if you have a *reflection* density of 1.36, then 4.365% is the *reflectance* of the tone area.

Density	Transmittance or Reflectance PER CENT	Density	Transmittance or Reflectance PER CENT	Density	Transmittance or Reflectance PER CENT
0.00	100.00	0.15	70.79	0.30	50.12
0.01	97.72	0.16	69.18	0.31	48.98
0.02	95.50	0.17	67.61	0.32	47.86
0.03	93.33	0.18	66.07	0.33	46.77
0.04	91.20	0.19	64.57	0.34	45.71
0.05	89.13	0.20	63.10	0.35	44.67
0.06	87.10	0.21	61.66	0.36	43.65
0.07	85.11	0.22	60.26	0.37	42.66
0.08	83.18	0.23	58.88	0.38	41.69
0.09	81.28	0.24	57.54	0.39	40.74
0.10	79.43	0.25	56.23	0.40	39.81
0.11	77.62	0.26	54.95	0.41	38.90
0.12	75.86	0.27	53.70	0.42	38.02
0.13	74.13	0.28	52.48	0.43	37.15
0.14	72.44	0.29	51.29	0.44	36.31

Density	Transmittance or Reflectance PER CENT	Density	Transmittance or Reflectance PER CENT	Density	Transmittance or Reflectance PER CENT
0.45	35.48	0.85	14.13	1.25	5.623
0.46	34.67	0.86	13.80	1.26	5.495
0.47	33.88	0.87	13.49	1.27	5.370
0.48	33.11	0.88	13.18	1.28	5.248
0.49	32.36	0.89	12.88	1.29	5.129
0.50	31.62	0.90	12.59	1.30	5.012
0.51	30.90	0.91	12.30	1.31	4.898
0.52	30.20	0.92	12.02	1.32	4.786
0.53	29.51	0.93	11.75	1.33	4.677
0.54	28.84	0.94	11.48	1.34	4.571
0.55	28.18	0.95	11.22	1.35	4.467
0.56	27.54	0.96	10.96	1.36	4.365
0.57	26.92	0.97	10.72	1.37	4.266
0.58	26.30	0.98	10.47	1.38	4.169
0.59	25.70	0.99	10.23	1.39	4.074
0.60	25.12	1.00	10.00	1.40	3.981
0.61	24.55	1.01	9.772	1.41	3.890
0.62	23.99	1.02	9.550	1.42	3.802
0.63	23.44	1.03	9.333	1.43	3.715
0.64	22.91	1.04	9.120	1.44	3.631
0.65	23.39	1.05	8.913	1.45	3.548
0.66	21.88	1.06	8.710	1.46	3.467
0.67	21.38	1.07	8.511	1.47	3.388
0.68	20.89	1.08	8.318	1.48	3.311
0.69	20.42	1.09	8.128	1.49	3.236
0.70	19.95	1.10	7.943	1.50	3.162
0.71	19.50	1.11	7.762	1.51	3.090
0.72	19.05	1.12	7.586	1.52	3.020
0.73	18.62	1.13	7.413	1.53	2.951
0.74	18.20	1.14	7.244	1.54	2.884
0.75	17.78	1.15	7.079	1.55	2.818
0.76	17.38	1.16	6.918	1.56	2.754
0.77	16.98	1.17	6.761	1.57	2.692
0.78	16.60	1.18	6.607	1.58	2.630
0.79	16.22	1.19	6.457	1.59	2.570
0.80	15.85	1.20	6.310	1.60	2.512
0.81	15.49	1.21	6.166	1.61	2.455
0.82	15.14	1.22	6.026	1.62	2.399
0.83	14.79	1.23	5.888	1.63	2.344
0.84	14.45	1.24	5.754	1.64	2.291

Density	Transmittance or Reflectance PER CENT	Density	Transmittance or Reflectance PER CENT	Density	Transmittance or Reflectance PER CENT
1.65	2.239	2.05	0.8913	2.45	0.3548
1.66	2.188	2.06	0.8710	2.46	0.3467
1.67	2.138	2.07	0.8511	2.47	0.3388
1.68	2.089	2.08	0.8318	2.48	0.3311
1.69	2.042	2.09	0.8128	2.49	0.3236
1.70	1.995	2.10	0.7943	2.50	0.3162
1.71	1.950	2.11	0.7762	2.51	0.3090
1.72	1.905	2.12	0.7586	2.52	0.3020
1.73	1.862	2.13	0.7413	2.53	0.2951
1.74	1.820	2.14	0.7244	2.54	0.2884
1.75	1.778	2.15	0.7079	2.55	0.2818
1.76	1.738	2.16	0.6918	2.56	0.2754
1.77	1.698	2.17	0.6761	2.57	0.2692
1.78	1.660	2.18	0.6607	2.58	0.2630
1.79	1.622	2.19	0.6457	2.59	0.2570
1.80	1.585	2.20	0.6310	2.60	0.2512
1.81	1.549	2.21	0.6166	2.61	0.2455
1.82	1.514	2.22	0.6026	2.62	0.2399
1.83	1.479	2.23	0.5888	2.63	0.2344
1.84	1.445	2.24	0.5754	2.64	0.2291
1.85	1.413	2.25	0.5623	2.65	0.2239
1.86	1.380	2.26	0.5495	2.66	0.2188
1.87	1.349	2.27	0.5370	2.67	0.2138
1.88	1.318	2.28	0.5248	2.68	0.2089
1.89	1.288	2.29	0.5129	2.69	0.2042
1.90	1.259	2.30	0.5012	2.70	0.1995
1.91	1.230	2.31	0.4898	2.71	0.1950
1.92	1.202	2.32	0.4786	2.72	0.1905
1.93	1.175	2.33	0.4677	2.73	0.1862
1.94	1.148	2.34	0.4571	2.74	0.1820
1.95	1.122	2.35	0.4467	2.75	0.1778
1.96	1.096	2.36	0.4365	2.76	0.1738
1.97	1.072	2.37	0.4266	2.77	0.1698
1.98	1.047	2.38	0.4169	2.78	0.1660
1.99	1.023	2.39	0.4074	2.79	0.1622
2.00	1.000	2.40	0.3981	2.80	0.1585
2.01	0.9772	2.41	0.3890	2.81	0.1549
2.02	0.9550	2.42	0.3802	2.82	0.1514
2.03	0.9333	2.43	0.3715	2.83	0.1479
2.04	0.9120	2.44	0.3631	2.84	0.1445

Density	Transmittance or Reflectance PER CENT	Density	Transmittance or Reflectance PER CENT	Density	Transmittance or Reflectance PER CENT
2.85	0.1413	2.90	0.1259	2.95	0.1122
2.86	0.1380	2.91	0.1230	2.96	0.1096
2.87	0.1349	2.92	0.1202	2.97	0.1072
2.88	0.1318	2.93	0.1175	2.98	0.1047
2.89	0.1288	2.94	0.1148	2.99	0.1023
				3.00	0.1000

Appendix II

RELATIVE EXPOSURE FOR ENLARGING OR REDUCING SIZE OF COPY

(Figures based on a known correct exposure for same size with no change in illumination.)

Reproduction Size (percent of original size)	Relative Exposure
10	.30
20	.36
25	.39
33	.45
40	.49
50	.56
60	.64
80	.81
100	1.00
150	1.60
200	2.25
300	4.00
400	6.25
500	9.00

Appendix III

FRACTIONS TO DECIMAL EQUIVALENTS OF AN INCH

FRACTIONS			Decimal Equivalent	FRACTIONS			Decimal Equivalent
64ths	32nds	Larger		64ths	32nds	Larger	
1			.0156	33			.516
2	1		.031	34	17		.531
3			.047	35			.547
4	2	$1/16$	.0625	36	18	$9/16$	.5625
5			.078	37			.578
6	3		.094	38	19		.594
7			.109	39			.609
8	4	$1/8$	.125	40	20	$5/8$	.625
9			.141	41			.641
10	5		.156	42	21		.656
11			.172	43			.672
12	6	$3/16$	.1875	44	22	$11/16$	.6875
13			.203	45			.703
14	7		.219	46	23		.719
15			.234	47			.734
16	8	$1/4$	.250	48	24	$3/4$	.750
17			.266	49			.766
18	9		.281	50	25		.781
19			.297	51			.797
20	10	$5/16$	.3125	52	26	$13/16$	.8125
21			.328	53			.828
22	11		.344	54	27		.844
23			.359	55			.859
24	12	$3/8$	.375	56	28	$7/8$	.875
25			.391	57			.891
26	13		.406	58	29		.906
27			.422	59			.922
28	14	$7/16$	.4375	60	30	$15/16$	.9375
29			.453	61			.953
30	15		.469	62	31		.969
31			.484	63			.984
32	16	$1/2$	.500	64	32	1	1.000

Appendix IV

METRIC-ENGLISH CONVERSION TABLES

METRIC-ENGLISH										ENGLISH-METRIC					
Cm.	In.	Cm.	In.	Cm.	In.	Cm.	In.	Cm.	In.	In.	Cm.	In.	Cm.	In.	Cm.
.1	.039	31	12.20	70	27.56	109	42.91	148	58.27	$^1/_{64}$	.040	23	58.42	62	154.48
.2	.079	32	12.60	71	27.95	110	43.31	149	58.66	$^1/_{32}$	.079	24	60.96	63	160.02
.3	.118	33	12.99	72	28.35	111	43.70	150	59.06	$^1/_{16}$	.159	25	63.50	64	162.56
.4	.157	34	13.39	73	28.74	112	44.09	151	59.45	$^1/_8$	.318	26	66.04	65	165.10
.5	.197	35	13.78	74	29.13	113	44.49	152	59.84	$^3/_{16}$	.476	27	68.58	66	167.64
.6	.236	36	14.17	75	29.53	114	44.88	153	60.24	$^1/_4$	.635	28	71.12	67	170.18
.7	.276	37	14.57	76	29.92	115	45.28	154	60.63	$^5/_{16}$	.794	29	73.66	68	172.72
.8	.315	38	14.96	77	30.31	116	45.67	155	61.02	$^3/_8$	.953	30	76.20	69	175.26
.9	.354	39	15.35	78	30.71	117	46.06	156	61.42	$^7/_{16}$	1.113	31	78.74	70	177.80
1.0	.394	40	15.75	79	31.10	118	46.46	157	61.81	$^1/_2$	1.27	32	81.28	71	180.34
2	.787	41	16.14	80	31.50	119	46.85	158	62.21	$^9/_{16}$	1.43	33	83.82	72	182.88
3	1.18	42	16.54	81	31.89	120	47.24	159	62.60	$^5/_8$	1.59	34	86.36	73	185.42
4	1.57	43	16.93	82	32.28	121	47.64	160	62.99	$^{11}/_{16}$	1.75	35	88.90	74	187.96
5	1.97	44	17.32	83	32.68	122	48.03	161	63.39	$^3/_4$	1.91	36	91.44	75	190.50
6	2.36	45	17.72	84	33.07	123	48.43	162	63.78	$^{13}/_{16}$	2.06	37	93.98	76	193.04
7	2.76	46	18.11	85	33.46	124	48.82	163	64.17	$^7/_8$	2.22	38	96.52	77	195.58
8	3.15	47	18.50	86	33.86	125	49.21	164	64.57	$^{15}/_{16}$	2.38	39	99.06	78	198.12
9	3.54	48	18.90	87	34.25	126	49.61	165	64.96	1	2.54	40	101.60	79	200.66
10	3.94	49	19.29	88	34.65	127	50.00	166	65.35	2	5.08	41	104.14	80	203.20
11	4.33	50	19.69	89	35.04	128	50.39	167	65.75	3	7.62	42	106.68		
12	4.72	51	20.08	90	35.43	129	50.79	168	66.14	4	10.16	43	109.22		
13	5.12	52	20.47	91	35.83	130	51.18	169	66.54	5	12.70	44	111.76		
14	5.51	53	20.87	92	36.22	131	51.58	170	66.93	6	15.24	45	114.30		
15	5.91	54	21.26	93	36.61	132	51.97	171	67.32	7	17.78	46	116.84		
16	6.30	55	21.65	94	37.01	133	52.36	172	67.72	8	20.32	47	119.38		
17	6.69	56	22.05	95	37.40	134	52.76	173	68.11	9	22.86	48	121.92		
18	7.09	57	22.44	96	37.80	135	53.15	174	68.50	10	25.40	49	124.46		
19	7.48	58	22.83	97	38.19	136	53.54	175	68.90	11	27.94	50	127.00		
20	7.87	59	23.23	98	38.58	137	53.94	176	69.29	12	30.48	51	129.54		
21	8.27	60	23.62	99	38.98	138	54.33	177	69.69	13	33.02	52	132.08		
22	8.66	61	24.02	100	39.37	139	54.72	178	70.08	14	35.56	53	134.62		
23	9.06	62	24.41	101	39.76	140	55.12	179	70.47	15	38.10	54	137.16		
24	9.45	63	24.80	102	40.16	141	55.51	180	70.87	16	40.64	55	139.70		
25	9.84	64	25.20	103	40.55	142	55.91	181	71.26	17	43.18	56	142.24		
26	10.24	65	25.59	104	40.95	143	56.30	182	71.65	18	45.72	57	144.78		
27	10.63	66	25.98	105	41.34	144	56.69	183	72.05	19	48.26	58	147.32		
28	11.02	67	26.38	106	41.73	145	57.09	184	72.44	20	50.80	59	149.86		
29	11.42	68	26.77	107	42.13	146	57.48	185	72.83	21	53.34	60	152.40		
30	11.81	69	27.17	108	42.52	147	57.87	186	73.23	22	55.88	61	154.94		

Appendix V

FILM COVERAGE WITH A CIRCULAR HALFTONE SCREEN

(Explanation) The horizontal and vertical scales around the outer edge of this chart indicate the linear dimensions of the film used. The diagonally placed numbers within the chart indicate the circular screen diameter.

The horizontal and vertical scales around the outer edge of this chart indicate the linear dimensions of the film used. The diagonally placed numbers within the chart indicate the circular screen diameter.

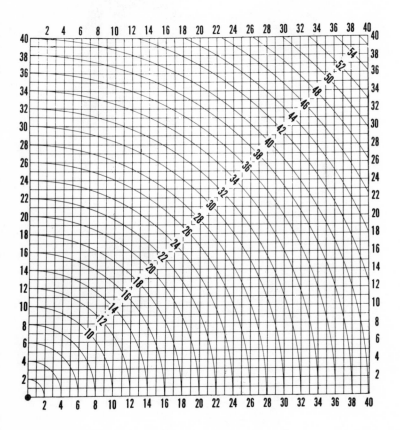

Appendix VI

NEW EQUIPMENT SUPPLEMENT—1964

Extensive research and development in photography has resulted in new equipment and new techniques. Although some of these are mentioned here, the photographer should constantly scan the literature for more recent developments.

*   *   *

Some of the newer light sources used by the industry include arc lamps with motor driven carbons, banks of incandescent bulbs operated at higher than normal voltage, pulsed Xenon lamps, and quartz-line lamps. Detailed information on each of these can be obtained from the supplier.

Courtesy Colortran Industries

Figure 66 Overvoltage
tungsten light source.

Courtesy nuArc Co., Inc.

Figure 67 Arc Lamp
with motor drive carbons.

Courtesy Macbeth Arc Lamp Co.

**Figure 68 Quartz
line light source.**

Courtesy American Speedlight Corp.

**Figure 69 Pulsed
Xenon lamps.**

DARKROOM SINKS

	Disadvantages	*Advantages*
Fiberglass	Susceptible to staining under certain conditions by color film processing chemicals. Cheaper brands not built with proper thickness of material.	One piece mold eliminates leaks. Impervious to most photo solutions. Easily cleaned. Neat appearance. Less susceptible to temperature variations. Designed with integral processing and inspection compartments.

Another method of temperature control in the sink is to employ either or both a thermostatically controlled refrigerating and heating device which warms or cools the water as required to the desired 68°F. After flowing around the trays of developer, short stop, and fixer in the sink, the water is discarded in the drain and is not recirculated.

Tanks or crocks holding mixed solutions of developer should be fitted with floating lids. These keep to a minimum the supply of available air which can oxidize the developer.

A number of suppliers furnish developers, fixers and other materials in concentrated liquid form. They may be in polyethylene bottles or in plastic lined cartons to which supply tubes can be attached. These are convenient to use and time saving.

Automatic Processing Equipment

There are many plants in which the total volume of all photographic work is such that automatic processing equipment can represent a profitable investment.

With these machines, exposed films are carried through the developer, hypo, wash and dryer automatically. The amount of time for the film to remain in the solution is preset and agitation and temperature controls are automatic. The use of this equipment allows the contact printer to concentrate on work requiring his highest skills and makes for maximum use and production from his exposing equipment.

There are nine manufacturers of automatic processing equipment. The machines fall roughly into two general types. The first is a continuous flow machine that can be likened to a belt or conveyor which carries the exposed film through the developer, hypo, wash and dryer.

The second type processes one or more batches of film at a time. The films are hung in racks attached to an overhead carriage. In operation, the racks are automatically lowered into and lifted out of tanks of developer, hypo and wash water according to a predetermined time cycle.

There are advantages in either type. With a continuous machine, films can be fed in immediately after exposure with no need to accumulate a batch. On the other hand, the batch type machine may be better suited for plants that regularly process films requiring different developers. In that case, tanks of the different developers can be placed in the machine's processing line. The machine, then, can be programmed to immerse the different batches of films in the suitable developer and skip over the tanks of the other developers.

Some thirteen models of automatic processors are built by the nine manufacturers. There are important differences in these various models to be considered in terms of the individual plant's requirements. Among many other factors, these differences include the type of transport system; allowable tolerance in temperature control; type of agitation; recirculation, filtration, and replenishment of solutions; over-all capacity and speed, provision of and type of dryer; time required for drying; and numerous other individual features, advantages and limitations.

Once they are established for a given machine, the processing variables are minimized in the plant's operations. But, this means that the photographer's lighting conditions and exposure times must also be more precise and standardized to meet the fixed requirements of the machine. In other words, compensation during processing for changes in exposure conditions can no longer be made. The experience of most plants using such equipment has been that when the requirements from the photographer have been worked out, results are usually much more consistent and as good as or better than the best of hand processing. The purchase of such a machine represents a substantial investment. However, many plants with sufficient volume of work have been able to amortize them in just a few years.

Manufacturers of automatic film processing equipment known to GATF at the time this volume was published are as follows:

Arkay Corp., 228 S. First Ave., Milwaukee 4, Wisc.

Charles Bruning Co., Inc. (Paragon Resolute Div.), 77 South Ave., Rochester 4, N. Y.

Copymation, Inc., 5650 N. Western Ave., Chicago 45, Ill.

Eastman Kodak Co., Rochester 4, N. Y.

Oscar Fisher Co., Inc., P. O. Box 426, Newburgh, New York.

LogEtronics, Inc., 500 E. Monroe, Alexandria, Va.

Pako Corp., 6300 Olson Memorial Highway, Minneapolis 40, Minn.

Reproduction Equipment Co., 1831 Levee St., Dallas 7, Texas.

Rolor Corp., Syosset Industrial Park, 155 Michael Drive, Syosset, L. I., N. Y.

INDEX

A

Aberrations and lens design, 154–155

Airy disc, 156

Angstrom Unit, 168

Angular variation of light intensity (see Exposure, miscellaneous information on)

Anti-halation backings (see Backings)

Arc, pulsed xenon (PXA) (see Lamps)

Arc lights
carbon, characteristics of, 28
characteristics of, 25–26
hints on uses of, 29
illumination requirements of, 28
spectral characteristics of, 28–29
types of, 26–27
types of carbon used in, 27
types of light generated by, 27

B

Backings, anti-halation, 190

Ballast resistor, 28

Balsam, Canada, 5

Basic flash exposure, 114

Bright-field illumination, diagram of set-up for, 53

Bright-field illumination technique, 53–54

C

Calibrated tapes, table of approximate distances for focusing with (see also Tapes, calibrated), 49

Calibrated wedge, setting the screen with (see Wedge, calibrated)

Callier factor, 121

Camera,
darkroom, 19
gallery, 19

Camera, focusing
by calibrated tape, 47–50
by ground glass, 46–47
by numerical counters, 50–51

Camera department
equipment of, 22–24
facilities of, 18–21
safety in, 37–38
tools of, 25–29

Camera techniques, special halftone
dropout negatives, 180
duotones, 183
image reversal, 190
indirect process of making halftone images, 187
opaquing masks, 186
procedure for shooting halftone positive, 189
re-screening halftone, 182
screen tints, 171

Camera test exposure, screen setting by (see Screen setting)

Canada balsam (see Balsam)

Carbro print, 40

Cell
photoelectric, function in light integrator, 35
selenium, function in exposure meter, 31–32

Ceric sulfate reducer (see Reducer)

Ceric sulfate solution (see Solution)

Chromatic aberration, 153–154

Chromium intensifier (see Intensifier)

Chromium intensifier formula (see Formula)

Color separation photography, halftone, 6

Coma, 154

Combination drawing, 40

Combination line and halftone shot, 65

Compensating glass, illustration of glass screen, 64

Compensator, glass screen, 64–65

Computation of the flash exposure, knowledge required for exact, 96

Computer, Du Pont shadow flash (see Shadow flash computer)

Constant movement diaphragm (see Diaphragm, constant movement)

Contact screen
description of, 6–7
development of, 106–107
gray (neutral), 110–111
magenta, 108–110
magnified section of, 6
making halftones with, 112
objections to, 107
orange, 108
principles of, 106
types of, 7–8

Copy, continuous-tone, 1

Copy, pin-cushion and barrel distortion of square, 153

Copyboard
illumination of, 131–134
used with exposure meter, 32–33

Cramer process developer (see Developer)

Crayon drawing, 39

Crossline screen
  disadvantages of, 106–107
  illustration of optics of, 87
Curvature of field, 154
Curve diagram, typical, showing transmission characteristics of a filter, 169

D

Dark-field illumination
  diagram of set-up for, 55
  technique for, 54–55
Darkroom
  entrances, 20–21
  entrances, illustrations of, 21
  equipment, miscellaneous, 25
  equipment of, 22
  operations, 19
  painting of, 19
  pressurization of, 21–22
  size of, 19–20
  tray storage space, 22
  typical, illustration of, 20
Darkroom camera (see Camera)
Darkroom sinks, comparison of, 22
Densitometer
  photoelectric, 129
  practical use of the, 130–131
  transmission, reflection and combination, 129–130
  uses of, 128
  visual, 128–129
Densitrometric terms and definitions, 120–121
Densitrometry and the densitometer, 120
Density
  and exposure, relationship between, 123
  meaning of, 120–121
  range, (see Densitometer)
  table, 195–198
  types of, 121
Developer
  Cramer process, 189
  DK50, 188
  lith-type, 24–25
Developer solution, temperature of, 11–16
Diaphragm, constant movement, 82
Diffraction
  theory, 67–71
  theory, comments on, 71
  theory, conclusions on, 72
Diffuse density (see Density, types of)
Distortion, 152
D logE curve variation due to increasing developing time, 126

Dog-eared stop
  description of, 80
  illustration of, 80
  making of the, 79–80
  screen distance with the, 81–82
  use of the, 81
  working of the, 80–81
Dot
  fringe, (see Halftone image)
  halftone, exposed through screen, 69
  highlight, 12–17
  shadow, 12–17
  vignetted silver, or dyed, 4
Dot formation
  according to the penumbral theory, isolux diagram showing, 74
  diffraction theory, diagram of, 67
  halftone, by the penumbral theory, illustration of, 73
Dropout negatives (See Negatives)
Dry transfer print, 39
Duotone
  definition of, 184
  preparing copy for, 184
  shooting primary negative, 184
  shooting secondary negative, 184
  types of copy referred to as, 183
  variations of, 185

E

Emulsion plane, evenness of illumination at, 134
Etching and chemical reduction (see Halftones, special processing procedures in making)
Exposure
  computer, illustration of Kodak Graphic Arts, 115
  importance of proper, 94
  large aperture, 180
  meter (see Meter)
  miscellaneous information on, 100–105
  observations on various stop systems, 98–100
  ratio of three-stop, 96–97
  ratio of two-stop, 97–98
  relative, for enlarging or reducing size of copy, 199
  relative, table for enlarging or reducing size of copy, 197
  single and multiple systems of, 94–95
  single-stop system, 95
  supplementary line, 180
  table of relative light intensity, 102

three-stop systems of, 95–96
two-stop system, 97
Exposure calculation, 137–138
Exposure changes for different magnifications (see Exposure, miscellaneous information on)

F

Failures, halftone, 103–105
Farmer's reducer, 142
Film area coverage with a circular halftone screen (see Halftone screen)
Films, storage of, 24
Filter chart for color contrast photography, 164
Filter factor
definition of, 165
determining, 166, 136–137
Filter stops (see Stops)
Filters
and light, 167–170
construction of, 163
definition of, 163
use in halftone photography, 163
Wratten, 163
Flash lamp (see Lamps)
Fluorescent lamp (see Lamps)
Focal plane, even illumination of, 134–135
Focusing
by calibrated tapes, 47–50
by ground glass, 46–47
by numerical counters, 50–51
the camera (see Camera)
with a screen in position, 63
Formula
chromium intensifier, 147
iodine-cyanide reducer, 143
mercury intensifier, 146–147
persulfate reducer, 146
special hardener, 147
Fractions to decimal equivalents of an inch, table of, 198
Fruwirth and Mertle, calculations of, 69

G

Gallery camera (see Camera)
Glass crossline screen
making a halftone with a, 8
manufacture of, 4–6
Glass halftone screen
care of, 59–60
conclusions on theory, 84–85
principles of, 59
rectilinear propagation and wave fronts, 66
theory of action of, 65–66
Glass screen

compensating glass, illustration of (see Compensating glass)
compensator (see Compensator)
operation as explained by the penumbral theory (see Penumbral theory)
ruling, diagram of, 17
shooting halftones with (see Halftones, shooting with the glass screen)
Goertz Artar Reversing Lens (see Lens, reversing)
Gray (neutral) contact screen (see Contact screen)
Gray scale, 9, 13, 36

H

H and D curve
plotting of, 123–128
shoulder of, 124
straight-line portion of, 124
toe of, 124
Halftone
color separation photography, 6
etching and carbon reduction, 140–141
failures (see Failures)
intensification of, 146
making with a glass crossline screen, 8
making with a Magenta Contact Screen, 13
methods, LTF studies of, 75
negative, schematic showing production of, 2
photography, originals for, 39–40
physical action of reduction of, 141–142
positive, procedures for shooting, 189
proportional reducers of, 145
special hardener—for after-treatment of films and plates, 147
special processing procedures in making, 140
Halftone image
dot fringe in, 52
evaluating halftone negative, 55
highly magnified section of a, 2
tonal range on the press for, 57–58
viewing dot fringe in, 52–53
Halftone image, indirect process for making
definition of, 187
need for, 187
preparation of, 187
Halftone reproductions, originals for,

description and handling of, 39
problems associated with kinds of copy, 40–43
types of, 39–40
Halftone screen
film area coverage with a circular, 202
illustration of a glass, 4
necessity of, 1
types of, 2–3
what it does, 3
Halftones, shooting, with the glass screen
exposure, 94–100
focusing the screen, 86–87
miscellaneous exposure information, 100–105
screen aperture to screen distance ratios, 88–89
screen ruling and the wavelength of light, 87–88
setting the screen, 89–93
Hardener, special, for after-treatment of films and plates (see Halftones, special processing procedure in making)
Highlighting method (see Contact Screen, Magenta)
Hislop's method of visual focusing (see Visual focusing)
Horgan's method of visual focusing (see Visual focusing)
Hypo solution, 12–17

I

Illumination, evenness of, calculating, 131
Image reversal
procedure, 190–192
when desired, 190
Image reverser
action of the prism, 192
straight line, 191
Incandescent lamp (see Lamp)
Indexing device, 9
Indirect process, hints for, 189–190
Ink sketch, 39
Integrating light (see Light integrator)
Integrating Light Meter, 10–16
Intensification (see Halftone, special processing procedures in making)
Intensifier
chromium, 147
mercury, 146
Iodine-cyanide reducer (see Reducer)
Iodine-cyanide reducer formula

(see Formula)
Iris diaphragm
description of, 78
illustration of, 78
working of, 78

K

Keystone Effect, 155
Kodak Screen
Magenta, 7
neutral tone, 7
Orange, 7

L

Lamps
arc lights, 149
flash, 10
fluorescent, 149
incandescent, 149
pulsed xenon arc, 149
yellow filter flash, 15
Large aperture exposures (see Exposures)
Lens aperture
and camera extension ratios by penumbral theory (see Penumbral theory)
and dot size by penumbral theory (see Penumbral theory)
Lens construction, typical, 151
Lens diaphragm, 10–16
Lens distances (see Table of Approximate Lens Distances)
Lens flare
and screen tints, 173
calculating percent, 161
Lens, process
field curve of, 154
flare in, 156–157
image distortion of, 155
job designed for, 148–151
lens aberration of, 155
resolution, 155–156
testing for flare in, 159
Lens, Reversing, Goertz Artar, 190
Lens stop (see Stops)
Light
sources of, 149
sources of, for process photography, 149
refraction of, 150
Lightroom
operations of, 18
painting of, 18
equipment of, 18–19
Light integrator
fall-off at various angles of incidence, 174
illustration of, 34
theory and construction of, 34–35

uses of, 35–36
Light intensity, angular variation of, 101–102
Light meter, integrating, 10–16
Light, nature of, 148–149
Light rays
  incident, 122
  reflected, 122
  transmitted, 122
Light table, 12
Light, theory of
  Greeks, ancient, 148
  Newton, Sir Isaac, 148
  Huygens, 148
  Young and Fresnel, 148
  Maxwell, 148–149
  Planck, 149
Light waves, diagram illustrating properties of, 167
Line stops (see Stops)
Lith-type developer (see Developer)

M

Magenta Contact Screen
  contrast and tone range with the, 112–113
  contrast control by use of colored filters with, illustration of, 109
  limitation of, 108–110
  making a halftone with a, 13
Magnification, percentage, determining (see Percentage magnification, determining)
Magnifier, 20-power, 10
Magnifiers (see Tools, photographer's)
Manually controlled arc light (see Arc light)
Mask, opaquing
  definition of, 186
  need for, 186
  preparation of, 186–187
Maze (see Darkroom)
Mercury intensifier (see Intensifier)
Mercury intensifier formula (see Formula)
Meter, exposure
  construction and theory, 31–32
  ways of using, 32–33
Meter, exposure, and light integrator
  correct uses of, 30
  illustration of, 31
Meter, integrating light, 10–16
Metric-English Conversion Table, 201
Mirror and prism
  advantages, 190–192

disadvantages, 190–192
Mirror, right angle prism or (see Prism)
Moiré pattern
  description of, 182
  illustration of, 182–183
Motor-driven arc light (see Arc light)
Mu, 168
Mounting angle of rectangular screens (see Rectangular screens)

N

Needle, etching (see Tools, photographer's)
Negative, continuous-tone, procedure for shooting
  exposure time, 188
  selection of developer, 188
  selection of film, 188
Negatives, failure of
  brown negatives, 105
  double dots and moiré, 104
  green brown negatives, 105
  incorrect contact, 103
  incorrect dot formation, 104
  spots, streaks and blotches, 105
  transparent dots fogged, 104
  variation in dot size and shape, 105
  weak, soft dots, 105
Negatives, dropout
  problems of producing, 180
  methods to use, 180
Neutral Test Card, Kodak, 31

O

Oil painting, 39
Orange Contact Screen (see Contact screen)
  Originals for halftone reproductions, description and handling of (see Halftone reproductions, originals for)
Originals
  grouping of by size, 43–45
  grouping of by tonal range, 45
Overlay mask method, 181

P

Paper, determining quality to use, 63
Pastel drawing, 39
Pencil drawings, 39
Pencil, grease (see Tools, photographer's)
Penumbral theory
  definition of, 72–73

glass screen operation as explained by the, 74–75
lens aperture and camera extension ratios by, 75
lens aperture and dot size by, 75–77
Percentage magnification, 43–45
Percentage magnification, determining, 44–45
Percent transmission, 136
Persulfate-permanganate reducer, (see Reducer)
Persulfate reducer formula (see Formula)
Photoelectric cell (see Cell)
Photoelectric densitometer (see Densitometer)
Photographer's tools (see Tools, photographer's)
Photographic print, 39
Photography, halftone color separation, 6
Pinhole theory, 84
Plates, storage of, 24
Positive, halftone, process for shooting, 189
Prism, mirror and (see Mirror)
Prism, right angle, or mirror, 190
Process lens (see Lens)

Q

Q Factor (see Callier factor)
Quantum theory, 149

R

Ratio of screen ruling (see Screen ruling)
Rectangular screens, mounting angle of, 61
Reducer
  action of, during dot-etching, 142
  ceric-sulfate, 144
  iodine-cyanide, 143
  persulfate-permanganate, 145
  proportional, 140
  subtractive, (see Halftone, special processing procedures in making)
  super-proportional, 145–146
Reduction, physical action of (see Halftone, special processing procedures in making)
Reflectance, 122
Reflection
  blinds for installation inside camera bellows, illustration of, 176
  density (see Density, meaning of)
Refraction

definition of, 150
index of, 150–151
law of, 150
Relationship between size of stop and dot size in even tints, 177
Relationship of lens aperture and dot size structures, 76
Relative exposure for enlarging or reducing size of copy, 199
Relative filter factor (see Filter factor)

S

Safelight
  illustration of setup of Kodak Adjustable, 114
  types of bulb for, 24
  uses of, 10, 14, 19
Safety in the camera department (see Camera department)
Screen, halftone (see Halftone screen)
Screen distance
  calculation of, 88
  for various screen rulings, 89
  illustration of aligning the screen and setting, 90
Screen ruling
  and tone values, 62–63
  determining size of to use, 62–63
  eclipse by, illustration of, 74
  ratio of, 60–61
  screen distances for various, illustration of, 89
  where generally used in lithography, 63·
Screen setting
  by camera test exposure, 93
  by visual focusing, 91
Screen tints (see Tints)
Sears Method, 180
Selenium cell (see Cell)
Shades (see Tones)
Shadow Flash Computer, Du Pont, 116
Single arc light (see Arc light)
Sink, darkroom (see Camera department)
Sketch, 40
Small stops for small dots (see Stops)
Solution
  ceric sulfate (from anhydrous ceric sulfate), 144
  ceric sulfate (from ceric bisulfate), 144
  sulfuric acid, 144–145
Special hardener formula (see Formula)
Special light source for protection

of even tints, 176
Specular density (see Density, types of)
Spherical aberration, 153
Square stop
  description of, 79
  working of, 79
Star-shaped stop (see Stops)
Stop, F64, use of, 103
Stops,
  detail, 95
  flash, 96
  highlight, 95
  middletone, 95
Stops, lens
  description of, 77
  purposes of, 77–78
Stop shape, to tint design, relationship between, 175
Stops, special, and controls
  constant-movement diaphragms, 82
  filter stops, 82–83
  star-shaped stops, 83
  line stops, 83
  small stops for small dots, 83–84
Stop systems, some observations on various, 98–100
Stops, various, illustrations of, 82
Super-proportional reducer (see Reducer)
Supplementary line exposure (see Exposure)
Sulfuric acid solution (see Solution)

T

Table, dot-etching, 23
Table of approximate lens distances,
  between lens and copy, 49
  between lens and film, 49
  total lengths between lens and image, 49
Tapes, calibrated, 9
Test Card, Kodak Neutral, 32
Technique, special halftone camera (see Camera)
Time-gamma curve (see H and D curve, plotting of)
Tints, screen
  developer, 179
  development factors, 174
  difficulties of producing even, 171
  lens flare and, 173
  light sources for, 172
  light variation with angular distance, 173–174
  suggestions for better, 175–179

typical procedure of producing, 172
  variations, 172
  vignetting, 173
Tints, screen, types of light sources for, 172–173
Tints, screen, suggestions for better
  additional hints, 177–179
  replacing lens with stop, 175
  using blinds to cut out stray reflections, 176–177
  using long bellows extension, 175
  using tungsten light source and double diffuser, 175–176
Tones, continuous, 1
Tone reproduction, effect of aperture on, 94
Tone values, screen ruling and (see Screen ruling)
Tools, photographer's, 36–37
Transmission density (see Density, meaning of)
Transmission, reflection and combination densitometer (see Densitometer)
Transmittance, 122
Trays, developing
  storage of, 22
  types of, 22
Turati Finder Stop (see Visual focusing)

V

Vacuum back, 10, 11, 14, 15
Vignetted dots (see Dots)
Visual densitometer (see Densitometer)
Visual focusing
  Hislop's method of, 93
  Horgan's method of, 91
  setting the screen by, 91
  Turati Finder Stop, 92

W

Wash, 40
Water bath, 9–14
Waterhcuse stop
  description of, 78
  illustration of, 78
  working of, 78–79
Water temperature control, 22
Wavelength chart, 168
Wave theory, 149
Wedge
  calibrated, 9
  setting the screen with a calibrated, 89–91
Wratten filter (see Filter)